Man and Number

DONALD SMELTZER

MAN AND NUMBER

COLLIER BOOKS
NEW YORK, N.Y.

This Collier Books edition is published by arrangement with Emerson Books, Inc.
Collier Books is a division of The Crowell-Collier Publishing Company

First Collier Books Edition 1962

Man and Number is also available in a hardcover edition published by Emerson Books, Inc.

First published 1958
All Rights Reserved
Hecho en los E.E.U.U.
Printed in the United States of America

PREFACE

In this book I have attempted to give some account of the development of man's use of number through the ages. The account covers the acquisition by early man of a sense of number and of systems of number words, and the transition from early methods of recording numerical information and carrying out calculations to those used at the present day. My aim has been to give some picture of the ways in which man's appreciation and use of number have grown, of the social and practical influences which have affected that growth, and of the place of number in the development of man's way of life. There is much about our present number system which, through familiarity, we have come to take for granted, but which, when we consider it more carefully, is seen to be in fact a remarkable achievement.

In a book of this size it has not, of course, been possible to pay attention to all related topics. I have not, for example, been able to include more than brief references to the closely related story of measurement, to number superstitions current at various times, or to the history of the more academic interest in numbers and their properties. Clearly these and other developments have influenced and have been influenced by man's facility with number, but to have dealt with them adequately would have required a much larger work.

I hope that the book will be of value to the general reader who is interested in human customs and their evolution. Extensive mathematical knowledge will not be needed in reading it: indeed for most of it a familiarity with only elementary mathematical ideas is necessary. For readers who wish to study further various aspects of the subject I have given a bibliography at the end of the book. The book should prove of value also to teachers in schools and to students training to be teachers. A knowledge of the ways in which the human mind first became aware of various elementary mathematical concepts and of the ways in which various devices and techniques evolved may give some insight into the best approach to the subject for young children to-day. I would not suggest that the young child's mind follows exactly the same lines of development as did the thought of man through the ages, but I do think that there is much to be learnt about the needs of children to-day from a study both of the ways in which earlier man progressed mathematically and of those concepts which proved difficult to him. It may be that some pupils in schools will find the book interesting and that some of the material in it will be found suitable for inclusion in classroom lessons. The historical approach can help children to see more fully the point of mathematical processes with which they are concerned.

I should perhaps make it clear that the illustrations of number symbols given in the book are not intended to be accurate reproductions from original documents; but I think they give a fair impression of the sort of symbols that were actually used.

My indebtedness to the writers referred to in the bibliography, and especially to Dr. D. E. Smith, will be apparent to anyone familiar with their works. I cannot claim any particular originality for the material which I have presented: my concern has been primarily to set it out in a simple and continuous manner, and I take full responsibility for what I have written. Such an attempt requires a many-sided approach and I have been fortunate in the help that I have received from several of my colleagues in King's College, Newcastle upon Tyne, from certain members of Her Majesty's Inspectorate who encouraged me to undertake this task, and from my publishers. I should like also to acknowledge help received at various stages from other colleagues, and from students and friends. I have had such ready assistance from so many people that it is not possible here to mention each individually. I should however refer to the part played by my wife, who has all along kept before me the point of view of the general reader and has helped in very many other ways. Without her help the book could not have been written.

D. S.

CONTENTS

Man and Number

CHAPTER I

MAN LEARNS TO COUNT

'... man has learned to aid his exceedingly limited perception of number by an artifice which was destined to exert a tremendous influence on his future life. This artifice is counting and it is to *counting* that we owe the extraordinary progress which we have made in expressing our universe in terms of number.'

'It is to his *articulate ten fingers* that man owes his success in calculation. It is these fingers which have taught him to count and thus extend the scope of number indefinitely.'

TOBIAS DANTZIG
in *Number: The Language of Science*

TO-DAY number is an essential part of our everyday thought and language. Numbers occur in prices, in weights, in measurements, in recipes, in cricket and football scores, and in fact in most familiar affairs of present-day life. We talk readily of *four* bars of chocolate, of a score of *seventeen*, of an audience of *two hundred and fifty*, and if we wish to write about these things we have the symbols *4, 17, 250*, to represent the numbers. Being ourselves so accustomed to meeting and using numbers, to thinking, speaking and writing about them, it is difficult for us to realize that there was a time when man had neither words nor symbols for four, seventeen and two hundred and fifty and, moreover, probably no conception of such numbers. We tend to regard a sense of number as an essential feature of the human mind, and number words and symbols as being fundamentally associated with any idea of number. Man's present facility with number has, however, developed from extremely limited beginnings. It is not possible to describe exactly the sense of number possessed by very early man, or to trace with any certainty the subsequent stages of development. But by considering

1

the possible origins of our number words and devices for
dealing with number, by referring to present-day primitive
tribes, and in other ways, it is possible to form some impression of the lines of development of man's facility with
number in prehistoric times. In this chapter I hope to give
a tentative picture of this development from early
beginnings to the use of counting systems.

Early Man's Sense of Number

We can only speculate about the mental powers of our
remote ancestors of the Old Stone Age living in Europe
perhaps some twenty thousand years ago. Any sense of
number which they possessed was probably very elementary,
but in their primitive way of life, a way of life which continued with little change for thousands of years, numerical
or precise quantitative issues would hardly arise. They were
essentially food hunters living in quite small groups with at
most a very limited form of speech. In their day-to-day life
no doubt problems arose which led to some consideration
of quantity and number. Their quantitative considerations
would be comparable to our 'is this enough?', rather than to
the more precise 'how much?'; in collecting food or fuel, for
example, experience may have taught them to know when
sufficient had been collected; this requires some intuitive
sense of amount but involves no idea of precise measurement. Any numerical ideas would probably be vague and
limited and confined to immediate concrete situations; they
may have been able to tell when the number of objects in a
group was increased or decreased—just as in some cases a
bird knows when an egg is removed from its nest; but like
the bird, they were probably only able to do this when the
group was very small.

Early man, with his vague and limited sense of number,
probably had no number words. We tend to think of number
words and symbols as essential to any idea of number, but in
fact it is possible to have some sense of number without
either, and without being able to count. This point can be
illustrated by referring to specific situations. We can see, for

example, that in building a simple hut, primitive men, unable to count, might feel quite confident that they had the necessary corner posts. As Max Wertheimer points out in 'Numbers and Numerical Concepts in Primitive Peoples', 'one can simply *know* that the framework depends upon "posts" and although the number is neither specified nor counted "these posts" are intrinsically involved in the idea of the hut'. In this 'knowing' there is some sense of number even though it is not conscious.

Tobias Dantzig in *Number: The Language of Science* tells an interesting story which illustrates a more conscious sense of number. A squire wished to catch a crow which had nested in a tower on his estate. As the crow always left its nest when anyone approached the tower and would not return until he left, the squire tried the ruse of having two men enter the tower and only one come out. The crow was not deceived, but stayed away until the second man came out. The experiment was repeated, first with three men and then with four, but without success. It was not until five men went into the tower and only four came out that the crow fell into the trap. Ornithologists may doubt the possibility of a crow's having such a sense of number or of its behaving so rationally. The story does, however, help us to imagine a numerical problem approached without the aid of any of the devices to which we automatically resort. The crow had no number words and no idea of counting; it did not make notches on a stick or lay twigs in a row one to correspond to each man; the men did not walk in triangular, square or other pattern formation. By some means depending only on direct vision it was able to distinguish between two men and three men, and between three men and four men. Any sense of number possessed by birds and animals must depend on direct vision and be independent of words and symbols. Professor O. Koehler of Freiburg, writing recently in the *Bulletin of Animal Behaviour* about his series of experiments with birds, expressed the belief that they *'learned to think unnamed numbers'*. His phrase expresses in another way this idea of a direct visual sense of number.

It is unlikely that very early man's direct visual sense of number was as great as that of the crow in Dantzig's story. At an early stage the human mind must have become aware of the distinction between one object and two objects, and between these and larger groups which were not distinguished from one another but merely gave a vague impression of 'many'. In a similar way young children to-day, having reached the stage of being able to recognize 'twoness', cannot until later distinguish between larger collections of things. To them collections of three or more things all appear to be 'a lot'—their direct visual sense only enables them to recognize a group of two, and they are not yet able to learn any other way of dealing with numbers. Man appears to have been at this stage for a vast period of time. It was only very gradually as human life developed and numerical considerations forced themselves on man's attention with increasing frequency that his conception of number became more definite and that he began to be able to recognize groups of more than two objects.

Number Sense and Number Words

As man's use of speech developed he no doubt began to give some expression to the simple ideas of number of which he had become aware. The use of number words followed and enhanced his conception of number. Early man's conception of number was vague, and probably for a long time he did not have words to refer solely to numerical ideas. Those aspects of 'twoness' which he recognized were probably referred to by different words—words which also indicated the ideas that we have in mind when we use such words as 'by', 'together', 'both' and 'other'.

Early man's conception of number was essentially related to particular situations; he had no conception of number apart from concrete objects. It is probable that even when dealing with concrete objects he had no general conception of number, and thus did not always use the same number words when referring to different types of object. To-day the words pair, couple and brace are all used to refer to two things; we talk of a couple, but not a pair or brace of eggs, and a pair, but not a brace or a couple of horses. This suggests that at one time our ancestors could see something in common between two horses and another two horses, but had not a sufficiently general conception of number to see something in common between two horses and two eggs. As a present-day example of this limited conception Dantzig mentions a tribe in British Columbia which has seven different sets of number words: one set for flat objects and animals; one for round objects and time; one for men; one for long objects and trees; one for canoes; one for measures and one, probably a later development, for counting when no definite object is referred to.

It is the ability to see something in common between two horses and two eggs, and between three pebbles and three days, that indicates a general conception of number. The 'twoness' and 'threeness' are recognized despite the differences in the objects concerned, just as the redness of a letter-box, a guard's flag and a ball is recognized, even though the objects differ in many other ways. By the time man had become sufficiently aware of 'threeness' to use a word for it, his conception of number seems to have been more definite and general—there do not appear to have been different words for different types of object or for different aspects of 'threeness'.

In most Indo-European languages the original significance of the word for 'three' was roughly 'over', 'across' or 'beyond'—due, one would imagine, to groups of three being formerly among those regarded as 'many', and later, when distinguished from other forms of 'many', still seen as more than, or beyond, groups of two. There is possibly a further linguistic indication of man's early awareness of only 'one', 'two' and 'many' in the distinction made in ancient languages and still retained in some modern languages, between the singular, dual and plural. The use of these three forms gives a particular emphasis to the ideas of one, two and many; as Bodmer suggests in *The Loom of Language*, it is as if we were to write cat, catwo and cats when referring to one, two and more than two cats.

While considering number words it is interesting to refer to the words used to express the cardinal and ordinal aspects of number. We to-day are aware of the relation between the cardinal aspect referring to the total in a collection, and the ordinal aspect denoting order or precedence. We show this when we use the symbols 1, 2, 3, 4—when the cardinal aspect is involved, and 1st, 2nd, 3rd, 4th—when referring to the ordinal aspect. We understand the symbol '20' on a packet of cigarettes to refer to a collection of *twenty* cigarettes, whereas the same symbol on a theatre seat refers to *one* seat —the twentieth in the row. But if we consider the words shown in the table below, we may wonder if man has always been aware of this relationship.

	one	first	two	second	three	third	four	fourth
Swedish	en	första	två	andra	tre	tredje	fyra	fjärde
German	ein	erste	zwei	ander or zweite	drei	dritte	vier	vierte
French	un	premier	deux	second or deuxième	trois	troisième	quatre	quatrième
Italian	uno	primo	due	secondo	tre	terzo	quattro	quarto

In each language the words for 'one' and 'first' are quite different from one another. The idea of 'first' emphasizing precedence or priority is, of course, far removed from that of only one being there. In Swedish and Italian and many other languages the words for 'two' and 'second' are also quite different, and though in modern German and French 'zweite' and 'deuxième' are formed from 'zwei' and 'deux', the older forms 'ander' and 'second' are quite different from the cardinal forms. The idea of 'second', of being next in order, is not necessarily immediately associated with the idea that the arrival or inclusion of the second brings the total up to two. Our word 'second', the French 'second' and the Italian 'secondo' derive from the Latin and originally signified 'following'; the original significance of the Swedish 'andra' and the German 'ander' was 'other'. For three and larger numbers there is usually a clear connexion between cardinal and ordinal names, and here again part at least of the explanation may be that the relation between these two aspects of number was adequately appreciated by the time that man began to express ideas of 'threeness' in words.

It is not easy for us to imagine the very limited facility with number possessed by early man. A delightful extract from Francis Galton's account of his experiences with the Damaras of South Africa may help us to form a clearer picture. It provides a vivid illustration of a people of recent times with a similarly limited facility.

'In practice whatever they may possess in their language, they certainly use no greater number than three. When they wish to express four they take to their fingers, which are to them as formidable instruments of calculation as a sliding rule is to an English schoolboy. They puzzle very much after five, because no spare hand remains to grasp and secure the fingers that are required for units. Yet they seldom lose oxen; the way in which they discover the loss of one is not by the number of the herd being diminished, but by the absence of a face they know. When bartering is going on each sheep must be paid for separately. Thus, suppose two sticks of tobacco to be the rate of exchange for one sheep, it would sorely puzzle a Damara to take two sheep and give him four sticks. I have done so, and seen a man take two of the sticks apart and take a sight over them at one of the sheep he was about to sell. Having satisfied himself that one was honestly paid for, and finding to his surprise that exactly two sticks remained in hand to settle the account for the other sheep, he would be afflicted with doubts; the transaction seemed to him to come too "pat" to be correct, and he would refer back to the first couple of sticks, and then his mind got hazy and confused, and wandered from one sheep to the other, and he broke off the transaction until two sticks were placed in his hand and one sheep driven away, and then the other two sticks given him and the second sheep driven away.'

The Limitations of Direct Visual Number Sense

Early number words were used to refer to recognized properties of groups of objects, i.e. they were essentially adjectival. The ability to recognize these properties I have referred to as a direct visual sense of number, and we have seen that from early vague awareness of only 'one', 'two' and 'many', man gradually developed a more definite sense of number and became able to recognize larger groups. He probably did not become clearly aware of 'threeness' until he had a fairly definite concrete conception of number and his recognition of 'fourness' came much later. In considering development beyond this stage we should note the limited extent of modern man's direct visual sense of number. This, as we will see, is difficult to assess, but the following test may help the reader to form some idea of his own direct visual number sense; the value of the test depends on the reader's ability to be honest with himself.

Instructions for test of the reader's direct visual sense of number

It is important to read all of these instructions carefully before turning over.

On page 10 there are diagrams of rows of the following articles: A, flowers; B, cubes; C, apples; D, match-stick men; E, crosses; F, sparrows; G, diamonds. After reading these instructions the reader should turn over to page 10, look quickly at row A and relying only on direct visual number sense try to say immediately how many flowers there are. There will be a strong temptation to count, or to allow the eye to break the row into two or more groups, but it is clearly important that this temptation should be resisted. A quick glance should be concentrated on the row as a whole and from the total impression received an attempt made to say how many there are.

After the row of flowers each of the following rows should be dealt with similarly in turn. It will help if the later rows are covered with a sheet of paper. As well as estimating how many things there are in each row the reader should note how confident he feels about his estimates.

Most people to-day can readily recognize collections of two, three and four objects and it is improbable that, in this test, anyone would have difficulty with rows A and D. Most people can also, though with more difficulty, recognize collections of five or even six or seven objects, though I have known many who were not confident about rows F and G after only a glance, and others who confessed that, despite their good intentions, they found themselves seeing row B as a group of three and a group of two. Few would, in fact, rely on direct visual number sense for collections of six and seven, and larger collections than these are almost impossible to assess accurately at a glance. If time is allowed for the eye to divide the row into groups of three it is possible to be confident about slightly larger collections, such as row C, but even this is difficult with row E, for there are too many groups of three. To find the number of crosses more easily we may point while counting. Some will count in ones, but most people possessing any facility with number will count in twos or threes. Very few would get the result more quickly by counting in fours or fives because though there would be fewer groups, the groups of two or three are much more readily recognized.

Except when dealing with small collections of objects we seldom rely on our direct visual sense of number. We may in attempting to estimate a length or distance try to see it as so many cricket pitch lengths or some other convenient and familiar unit which is not contained in it too many times. But usually, when numerical considerations arise, we automatically resort to some device such as grouping,

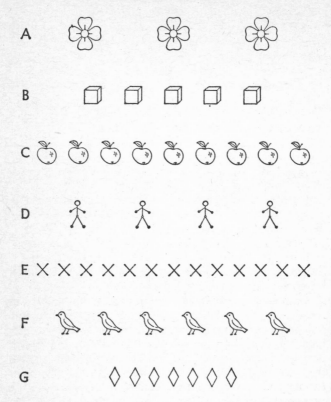

pattern forming, tallying or counting as an aid or alternative to our direct visual sense. The use of pattern forming and grouping is illustrated opposite where collections used in the test are arranged in familiar pattern formation (rows A, B and D), in rows and columns of appropriate size (rows C and E) and in repeated pattern formation (rows F, G and E).

As most people to-day seem to find some difficulty in recognizing groups of more than four or five objects, it is improbable that early man proceeded beyond 'fourness' as long as he relied mainly on his direct visual sense in numerical

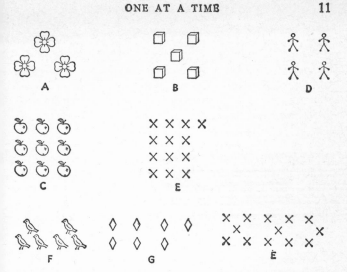

situations. We do not know to what extent, if any, pattern forming and grouping were used by early man. An occasional genius may have become vaguely aware of their value but it is unlikely that their use became widespread. In any case their scope is limited if the number of things in a column, the number of columns and the number of patterns have to be recognized by direct vision; and, of course, more than five objects do not form obvious patterns. The other two devices, tallying and counting, have, however, played a very important part in the development of man's facility with number.

One at a time

Tallying was probably one of the first devices which man used when he began to take a more extensive interest in the size of collections. In tallying instead of trying to assess a collection as a whole the objects forming the collection are taken one at a time and a tally placed to correspond to each of them. Any convenient objects such as pebbles or twigs may be used as tallies—or instead scratches may be made on the ground, or notches cut in a stick; our word 'tally' comes from the Old French 'taille' (cut or notch), from which developed the modern French 'tailler' (cut) and 'tailleur' (tailor). When pebbles are placed in a row, one to correspond to each sheep passing through a gate, the final collection of pebbles represents the flock numerically and is more convenient to deal with than the actual flock. As the sheep are taken one at a time there is no particular difficulty in tallying a large flock—it is merely necessary to have a large number of pebbles. But though tallying is of practical value in particular situations, it does not lead to any convenient and general means of reference. To find if one flock is as large as another one it is more convenient to refer to the substitute collections of pebbles than to the actual sheep, but this could be a very tedious process.

To us, then, tallying and similar devices involving one-to-one correspondence seem simple though cumbersome means of answering, in particular situations, such questions as 'are they all here?' or 'are there enough?'. They do not provide an answer to the more general question 'how many are there?'. These points are further illustrated by the story of the man who had recently moved into a new house and was lying in bed one night planning to lay the stair carpet the next day. He remembered that he did not know whether he had a sufficient number of stair rods and realizing that this would be the first problem to tackle he planned to place one rod on each stair in turn until he reached the top or had used all the rods. At that point he fell asleep. When he awoke next morning he realized that it would be much simpler to count the rods and count the stairs. His earlier idea would, however, have answered his particular question and would have been applicable however many stairs there were. But it would not have provided any general means of reference; for example, he could only have found if he had sufficient pads for all the stairs by going right through a similar one-to-one performance.

To early man tallying would be of great practical service when more than three or four things were involved. It would, for example, help him to check his possessions and to keep a record of the passage of time. The idea of a group of animals being represented numerically by a collection of pebbles would seem far from simple to him, of course, and his use of tallies can only have developed tentatively and gradually, but all peoples in whose way of life numerical considerations came to be of some importance appear to have taken to tallying in some form.

It is not only in tallying that man has used one collection to represent another one numerically. This idea is also involved in the association of particular numbers with certain familiar objects—an association which can form a useful aid to recollection and reference. For example, if it is seen that in a collection of eggs there is one to correspond to each of the leaves of a clover, or the fingers of the hand, the association with the clover, or the hand, will provide a means of remembering and referring to the size of the collection. The following diagrams suggest other possible associations—the

association of 'twoness' with the wings of a bird and 'fourness' with the legs of an animal. These familiar objects may be regarded as 'model collections' each of whose parts corresponds with one of the objects in the collection under consideration. This association with model collections may lead to such number words as 'wings' (two), 'clover' (three), 'legs' (four), and 'hand' (five). As we shall see later, the number words used by some primitive peoples originated in this way and it is possible that some of our number words did so too.

It was not, however, tallying or association with 'model collections' which led to the most far-reaching developments in man's facility with number. Tallying provided a means of dealing with large collections but no means of reference.

Association with 'model collections' may have led to convenient means of reference but, as few familiar objects suggest numbers greater than five, its use was limited to small collections. It was through the use of a special set of tallies—the fingers—that it became possible both to deal with large collections and to refer to their size.

The Fingers

Man may at a very early stage have used his fingers to express numbers, for in his attempts to communicate with his fellows gestures were probably at least as important as sounds. We can imagine him trying, for example, to indicate that he had seen three horses by holding up or pointing to three fingers while indicating 'horse' by some recognized sound or gesture. When later man took to tallying, his fingers formed a convenient set of tallies which always went with him. True, the fingers are limited in number, but as we shall see this is an advantage rather than otherwise—and they have the important advantages that they are readily distinguished from one another and that being attached to the hands they always remain in the same order. These two advantages make it possible, in finger tallying, to refer to the size of a collection.

In many languages number words have come from this reference to the fingers. This connexion is more apparent today in some primitive languages than in modern European languages. Benchara Branford in *A Study of Mathematical Education* gives the etymological significance of the number words used by the American Indians of the Pueblo of Zuni:

One	=	taken up to start with
Two	=	put down together with that which
Three	=	partner equally itself which does
Four	=	all of the fingers all but done with
Five	=	the notched off.

The following further examples of the literal meanings of number words are taken from primitive languages in various parts of the world.

5 'whole hand', 'once my hand', or simply 'hand'.
6 'one on the other hand', 'cross over', 'other one'.
7 'he pointed'.
8 'fold down fingers which are two' or 'fold down two'.
9 'fold down finger which is one' or 'fold down one'.
10 'both hands', 'hands across'.
11 'one on the foot'.
13 'my hands three besides'.
15 'whole foot'.
16 'one on the other foot'.
18 'finished my hands pass to my other foot three'.
20 'a man brought to an end', 'my hands, my feet' or simply 'man'.
21 'one to the hands of the next man'.
40 'two men'.
100 'five men'.

From these examples one gets a picture of an elaborate procedure in which, one at a time, the objects of a collection are associated with the corresponding fingers (or toes) and the final position is described by an expression which in some cases is cumbersome. In general the expressions used describe either the total collection of fingers (e.g. 'both hands')—in this case the fingers may be said to form model collections—or the last individual finger used (e.g. 'he pointed'). The latter form is possible because of the difference mentioned between the fingers and other objects used as tallies. Pebbles used as tallies may all be more or less alike, but fingers can easily be distinguished from one another and always remain in the same order. Hence, in finger tallying it is possible to notice and remember the last finger used and later, if the fingers are used in a consistent order, to recall the size of the collection by referring to this finger. If, for example, in tallying a group of horses, the last horse to pass is found to correspond to the middle finger of the second hand, this fact is sufficient to make reference to the size of the group possible. Here the group of horses is associated not with the corresponding group of fingers, but with one individual finger. As an individual finger can be associated with the place in an order or sequence as well as with the size of a collection, i.e. with the eighth horse as well as a group of eight horses, finger tallying probably helped to draw attention to the connexion between the cardinal and ordinal aspects of number.

Though the use of the fingers (and sometimes the toes) is a development characteristic of all peoples who passed beyond the most elementary use of number, all number words do not, of course, derive from the fingers. As we have seen, man may have become aware of the lower numbers before he took to any form of tallying. We get a useful picture of the development of number language by considering the following number words used by the Abipones of America (from de Villiers' *The Numeral Words*)

1 iñitara	5 neènhalek or hanamhegem
2 iñoaka	10 lanàmrihegem
3 yekaini	20 lanàmrihegem cat gracherhaka
4 geyenkñate	anamichirihegem.

The first three words are used only as number words. One imagines that they had, at one time, some significance other than a numerical one but their use having begun much earlier than the other number words their original meaning has been forgotten. The words 'geyenkñate' and 'neènhalek' are names of familiar objects which are used to denote numbers. The objects which suggest four and five to the Abipone would hardly have occurred to us; 'geyenkñate' means the toes of the American 'ostrich' (there are three in front and one behind) and 'neènhalek' a beautiful skin with spots of five different colours. 'Hanamhegem', an alternative word for five, and the expressions for ten and twenty mean respectively 'the fingers of one hand', 'the fingers of both hands' and 'the fingers of both hands and both feet'.

Because of the great antiquity of our number words their origin cannot be traced with certainty. It has been found, however, that in most early Indo-European languages, the first four number words were declined while words for the numbers from five to ten were not declined. It has been suggested that this difference is due to the words for the lower numbers being much older. As I have already mentioned, these words probably evolved gradually from words which had only a vaguely numerical significance. In time they came to be used only as number words and their original significance was forgotten. They were, however, essentially adjectival—they referred to a recognized property of a group of objects—and hence were declined. The higher number words were probably in the nature of finger names in inverted commas and thus were not declined; they were treated as nouns which were not related to the subject in the way that an attributive adjective would have been. A more detailed consideration of the possible origins of the lower number words is given by Lilian M. Bagge in an article on 'The Early Numerals' in the *Classical Review* (Vol. XX), 1906.

There have been various attempts to relate European number words to finger counting. Some writers, for example, have pointed to the resemblance between the Gothic 'taihun' for ten and 'twai handus' for two hands and between the German 'zehn' for ten (Old German 'zehan') and 'zwei hand' for two hands; it has been suggested that 'twenty' comes from 'twain of tens'. There can be no certainty about such points; our number words are of such great age that any suggestions about their original meaning can only be conjectural.

Counting

As man gradually became more accustomed to dealing with number, finger tallying probably became less slow and elaborate. The expressions which he used to refer to the position reached in his tallying probably became simpler too; with primitive tribes to-day one usually finds that those tribes with only an elementary conception of number use full descriptive expressions, while those with a greater conception tend to use shortened forms. In modern counting, number words are used without the intermediate association with the fingers. But the essential features of finger tallying still remain. In counting, words are used as tallies, and as in other tallying, the objects are taken one at a time. One word is associated with each object in turn, and it is possible to indicate the size of the whole collection by giving the word associated with the last object.

The important features of counting may be illustrated as follows. If to indicate how many books there are in a pile I merely say:

'book, book, book, book, book, book, book'

this is equivalent to placing pebbles in a row:

●   ●   ●   ●   ●   ●   ●

as the words, like tallies, cannot be distinguished from one another, no simple means of reference is possible. And it is not sufficient merely to distinguish them thus:

'red book, blue book, white book, brown book, green book, black book, yellow book'.

This gives more information about this particular pile of books and anyone who remembers this information will be in a position similar to that of the shepherd who can tell if all his sheep are there because he remembers their faces. But the information is not numerical in any general sense and there is still no simple means of reference; to give the expression associated with the last book would not help us at all in comparing this pile with another pile of books.

If, however, I say:

'one book, two books, three books, four books, five books, six books, seven books',

a concise and general means of reference is possible. This is equivalent to tallying with the fingers,

and as the words like the fingers are used in a consistent order, the expression

'seven books'

is, like the finger name 'he pointed', sufficient to enable this pile to be compared with others and with groups of other objects. It may be said that as when counting we are referring to individual books in turn, ordinal names,

'first book, second book, third book, fourth book, fifth book, sixth book, seventh book',

should really be used and the fact that there are seven books deduced from the fact that the last is the seventh. This is strictly correct though no one actually uses the ordinal words.

Counting, then, is quite a complex process, and early man's use of one of the lower number words to describe a recognized property of a small group of objects should not be mistaken for counting. In considering counting I have so far referred to the way in which number words are used in an agreed order and the size of a collection indicated by the word associated with the last object in the collection. But if we could only count to a hundred by using a hundred unrelated number words, counting would make enormous demands on the memory. A further important feature of counting is that the number words are related according to a definite system or pattern. Thus 'twenty-four' is a composite expression indicating two tens and four. In such expressions we have the important idea of a *collective unit*.

The idea of a collective unit can be illustrated by considering a shepherd tallying sheep on his fingers. He will come to the last finger on his second hand when only ten sheep have passed. If, however, a second shepherd raises one of his fingers each time the first shepherd uses all his fingers, the pair of them will be able to tally any number up to a hundred (strictly speaking, a hundred and ten). The second shepherd is here recording not single sheep but tens of sheep—ten sheep together being taken as a collective unit.

The collective unit is a fundamental aspect of all number systems. It is possible that man made some use of the idea even before he took to finger tallying. There are primitive tribes to-day who have independent number words for only one and two but are able to refer to groups of up to six objects. The expressions they use after two have the following significance:

3   two and one
4   two twos (or two and two)
5   two twos and one
6   two twos and two.

Two objects are thus taken as a collective unit. Beyond six there are too many twos for precise comprehension, and larger groups are all referred to as 'many'. It has been said that with these peoples a sense of parity is so much stronger than their number sense that they will notice for example if one object is removed from a row of eight but will rarely notice if two are removed, as this still leaves a number of complete pairs.

When number words are formed by regarding two objects as a collective unit the system of number words is said to have a *base* two or to be a binary system. Similarly in a system with a base five, a quinary system, the number words refer to the number of groups of five and the number of single objects left over. Our expression 'twenty-four' refers to the number of tens and units because we use a system with a base ten, a decimal system; on a quinary system the same number of objects would be referred to by a name meaning 'four fives and four'.

A primitive example of a quinary system is provided by the Joloffs of Africa; their first ten number words are:

1 wean	6 judom wean	(5 and 1)
2 yar	7 judom yar	(5 and 2)
3 yat	8 judom yat	(5 and 3)
4 yanet	9 judom yanet	(5 and 4)
5 judom	10 fook.	

In other similar examples the expression for six signifies 'five plus one' or simply 'plus one' and in some the expression for four, like the Roman IV, indicates that it is one less than five.

All peoples who had to make much use of number appear, sooner or later, to have developed number systems with a base 5, 10 or 20. At an early stage some systems of number words were formed in which 2, 3 or 4 may be said to have been the base, and later the use of systems with 12 as base was fairly widespread, particularly in connexion with measurement. But in all cases, owing to the importance of the fingers in man's dealing with numerical problems, one of the systems based on finger tallying was eventually established as common custom. The advantage of collective units based on finger tallying is due to the number of fingers being limited and always the same. In tallying with pebbles it is possible to regard an agreed number of pebbles as a collective unit but the agreed number is an arbitrary matter; in finger tallying the agreed number is fixed and the tallier automatically knows when that number has been reached. The number expressions from primitive languages given on page 15 provide examples of the use of 5 (a hand), 10 (both hands) and 20 (hands and feet) as collective units or bases.

The early people who used the idea of a collective unit had not a real conception of a number system. What they used was the result of gradual evolution and not deliberate planning. An interesting example of an early system of number words is found in the Yorkshire dales. The words, believed to be of Celtic origin, were still used by some shepherds a generation ago and may still be used by some to-day. It has been suggested that the words are a relic from those Britons who were left behind in the dales when Anglo-Saxon invaders drove most of their fellows still further westwards. The survival of these number words while other words perished is attributed to their connexion with that ancient and enduring occupation—agriculture—and to the stability of number words. One version of the words is as follows:

1 yan	6 sethera
2 tyan	7 lethera
3 tethera	8 hovera
4 methera	9 dovera
5 *pimp*	10 *dick*

11 yanadick	16 yanabumfit (or yanabum)
12 tyanadick	17 tyanabumfit (or tyanabum)
13 tetheradick	18 tetherabumfit
14 metheradick	19 metherabumfit
15 *bumfit*	20 *jiggit.*

There is a delightful rhythm about these words—'a poetic jingle' as one writer has described it. They go in rhyming pairs with, after every second pair, a rather explosive and quite markedly different word to denote the completion of a five or a hand. The similarity between 'yan' and words in other languages denoting unity such as 'one', 'ein', 'un' is striking; in 'tyan' and 'tethera' one detects a suspicion of 'that one' and 'the other', and even more of the dialect forms of these expressions. There are many local variations of the set of words given above, variations due to local pronunciation and to the fact that for centuries they have been preserved only by word of mouth. There is a definite resemblance between these words and the Welsh number words. Similar examples might have been given from Cumberland, Westmorland and Lincolnshire. In all the pattern is the same. There are separate words from one to ten as in a decimal system. From ten onwards the words for ten and fifteen are in turn combined with the words for one, two, three and four—this and the emphasis of every fifth gives the system a quinary flavour. There do not appear to have been words beyond twenty; twenty sheep were probably taken as a unit (as in a vigesimal system) and a pebble placed for every twenty counted.

Most advanced peoples have for long used number systems with primarily a decimal base, but the use of the base 20 has left impressions in many languages. Our word 'score' for twenty possibly derives from tallying by making notches in a piece of wood, with every twentieth a deeper notch or score. In French and Danish counting to-day there are clear relics of counting in twenties. The significance of the French words from 60 to 100 is as follows:

| 60 sixty | 61 sixty and one |

62 sixty two	81 four twenties one
. . .	82 four twenties two
. . .	
69 sixty nine	. . .
70 sixty ten	. . .
71 sixty and eleven	89 four twenties nine
	90 four twenties ten
. . .	91 four twenties eleven
75 sixty fifteen	
	. . .
. . .	95 four twenties fifteen
78 sixty ten eight	
79 sixty ten nine	. . .
80 four twenties	98 four twenties ten eight
	99 four twenties ten nine.

In some French documents of the Middle Ages the writing of numbers also shows the influence of twenty as base; there is for example IIII^{xx} for eighty and VI^{xx}XI for one hundred and thirty-one. The fact that in French and in some Germanic languages the number words after sixty are formed in a different manner from the lower number words may be connected with the use at one time of a base of sixty; as we will see in the next chapter, the Babylonians used a sexagesimal system, and this influenced the customs of later peoples.

The Danish words for 20, 30 and 40 denote, as ours do, 2, 3 and 4 tens.

1 en	10 ti	60 tres
2 to	20 tyve	70 halvfjerds
3 tre	30 tredive	80 firs
4 fire	40 fyrre	90 halvfems
5 fen	50 halvtreds	100 hundrede

But 'tres' and 'firs' for 60 and 80 are shortened forms of 'tresindstyve' and 'firsindstyve' which mean 'three times twenty' and 'four times twenty'. 'Halvtreds' for 50 is a shortened form of 'halvtredsindstyve' meaning 'half three times twenty'. Here 'half three' means $2\frac{1}{2}$, its significance perhaps being 'half way to three'. Similarly 'halvfjerds' and 'halvfems' denote $3\frac{1}{2}$ and $4\frac{1}{2}$ twenties.

Vigesimal systems were also prominent in early civilizations in America. In the ancient Maya civilization of Central America a number system was used which was almost, but not entirely, worked on a base of twenty. The Aztecs too, used a system which was primarily vigesimal but which also involved a subsidiary decimal system. These two systems will be considered again in the next chapter on written numerals. In Scots Gaelic a vigesimal system is still used —thus 'da fhichead' for forty means literally 'two twenties'.

These examples all refer to systems developed from the use of the fingers. There are, however, examples of the use of 12 as a base. We still count eggs in dozens, we have 12 inches in the foot and 12 pence in the shilling, there were 12 ounces in the old pound. It may be that the words 'eleven' and 'twelve'—irregularities in our present system of number words—are due to an earlier duodecimal system (i.e. a system with a base 12). They and the equivalent words in some other Indo-European languages appear originally to have meant 'one left' and 'two left'—left, that is, to be counted after all the fingers had been used. It seems, for example, that the Gothic words were 'áinlif' and 'twalif' and the cognate Old English forms 'en(d)le(o)fan' and 'twelf'— the latter coming probably from the earlier 'twalif'. There are obvious advantages in the use of 12 as a collective unit as it can be divided into halves, thirds, quarters and sixths without the use of fractions. But such considerations on the whole weighed less with man than the more immediate practical considerations concerned with tallying.

The idea of the collective unit, so important a feature of counting, can be extended further than I have indicated in the above examples. This extension can be illustrated by referring again to our shepherds. Two shepherds each using ten fingers were able to indicate any number of sheep up to a hundred. If these two are joined by a third who raises one finger each time the second shepherd uses all his fingers, this third shepherd will record tens of tens of sheep. As he can tally ten of these new units the three shepherds between them will be able to tally any number of sheep up to a thousand. Similarly a fourth shepherd would record units of a thousand sheep and so on. Another illustration of the same principle is provided by the milometer on a car or cycle, where each wheel moves one place every time its neighbour to the right completes a revolution by moving ten places. The first wheel records units, the second tens, the third hundreds, and so on.

This extension of the idea of a collective unit enables counting to be continued indefinitely with only the introduction from time to time of a new name for the next collective unit. It would seem that no system with a base five has ever been developed in this way; few peoples using this base have even proceeded as far as five fives and four. And though, as we shall see in the next chapter when we consider written number systems, both decimal and vigesimal systems have been developed in this way, the development was a late one. It is possible, without this development, to refer to over a hundred objects on a decimal system, and to over four hundred objects on a vigesimal system. It would be difficult for peoples whose use of number was mainly verbal to think about numbers much larger than these, and in their way of life there would be little need to do so; it is interesting to note that the present-day Crow-tribe of the North American prairie do not usually count higher than a thousand, as they say that honest people have no use for higher numbers. The evolution of counting, a process which is now an essential part of our mental equipment, was slow and gradual. The impetus for this evolution came from man's needs in checking his possessions, in barter and in his attempts to devise a workable calendar. It was not until man began to form settled communities that it became increasingly necessary to deal with large numbers. In these communities written number systems were developed and man's number range extended; the extension was, however, only gradual—in most languages, for example, the word for a thousand is of much later origin than the word for a hundred.

Finger Symbols

Long after decimal counting systems were well established as a means of tallying in *words* and referring by a single *word* to the size of a collection, fingers were commonly used in man's dealings with number. For many centuries they were used by many different peoples as a convenient method of denoting numbers, and various quite elaborate systems of finger symbols were evolved. The Chinese, for example, used, and in some cases still use, the following finger numerals. For 1 the thumbnail of the right hand touched the outside of the first joint on the little finger of the left hand; for 2 and 3 the second and third joints were touched in the same way. Having thus passed up the outside of the fingers for 1, 2 and 3, the thumb passed down the middle of the finger touching the joints in the reverse order for 4, 5 and 6 and then back again up the inside of the finger for 7, 8 and 9. With the next finger the same position denoted the corresponding multiples of 10, with the middle finger 100s, and so on. Chinese merchants at one time carried on their bargaining by touching one another's hands in this way, their cloaks keeping the matter a secret.

The Chinese finger symbolism clearly fits admirably with a decimal system of counting. European finger symbolism was not so simple and systematic. The Romans, in about the first century A.D., had a finger symbolism by which numbers up to 10,000 could be represented; the Greeks had a similar system as early as the fifth century B.C. though we do not know exactly what the signs were. Finger numerals similar to those used by the Romans were commonly used throughout Europe until perhaps four hundred years ago. For many they were the chief means of dealing with numerical problems, and at the great international fairs merchants who spoke different languages were able to carry on their bargaining by making these number signs with their fingers. So general was their use that only a few centuries ago all European manuals of arithmetic gave full instructions in finger symbolism, and it is interesting to note that in the eighth century the Venerable Bede, in writing a treatise on 'the reckoning of times' (i.e., the calculation of Easter, etc.), devotes his first chapter to explaining the method of showing numbers with the fingers. The chapter is headed 'Concerning counting or the speech of the fingers' and begins, 'We have considered it necessary (with God's help) to write about the measurement of time, and first of all to explain briefly the useful and convenient skill of bending the fingers . . .'.

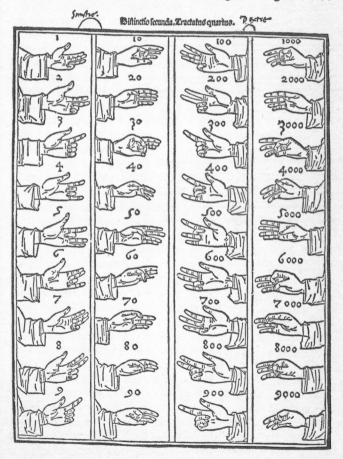

After more introductory remarks he proceeds, 'When therefore you say One, by bending the smallest finger in the left hand, you place the joint in the middle of the palm'. He gives a description of the method of representing all the numbers from one to ten and all the multiples of ten; in this description he refers to the middle fingers as the Doctor and those on either side of it as the Index finger and the Unchaste finger. The illustration of finger numerals shown on page 27 is from a manual of the fifteenth century. Though there were variations, particularly in denoting large numbers, this illustration is fairly representative—the position shown for thirty is clearly the same as Bede's: 'When you say thirty you join the nails of the index finger and the thumb in a close embrace'. The numbers from one to nine were indicated by using the first three fingers of the left hand either extended, bent at the middle joint or closed to the palm; in Bede's account the same nine positions with the right hand indicated the corresponding multiples of a thousand (in the illustration these positions denote hundreds). For multiples of ten the index finger and thumb of the left hand were used, and the same positions on the right hand represented the corresponding multiples of a hundred. Having described all this, Bede then describes how the left hand placed in various positions on the chest, navel, thigh or loins represents ten thousands or multiples of ten thousand, and how the right hand placed in similar positions represents the corresponding multiples of a hundred thousand.

To-day the gesture language of number is used sometimes to give emphasis but it is much less important than in earlier times. The schoolboy's fingers may help his surreptitious communication of answers in the arithmetic class, and many children and adults resort to their fingers as an aid to reckoning, but the reduced status of the fingers is clear from the furtive and rather ashamed way in which this is usually done. The decimal basis of our number system remains, however, as a permanent monument to the great part played by the fingers in the development of man's facility with number.

CHAPTER II

NUMBER RECORDING

Stone Age engraving on bone
(from the cave of La Mairie, Teyjat, Dordogne, France)

In the previous chapter we have seen something of the way in which the gesture and spoken languages of number developed. We turn now to the evolution of the written language of number—the way in which man learnt to make visible marks to convey numerical information. It is difficult to decide when such a practice can really be considered to have begun. Many of the drawings and paintings left by Stone Age man depict animals—in some, one may wonder if the artist has attempted to show how many had been caught or it was hoped to catch. It is unlikely that they were attempts to give precise numerical information but in some there was at least the intention to indicate 'many'. And long before writing was invented, man began to make marks to record 'how many' more precisely. Marks scratched on a rock, painted on a wall or cut in a stick or tree trunk were used as tallies in the simple type of tallying described in the previous chapter. Such marks were the beginnings from which written number systems grew.

But, though men at quite an early stage made marks to indicate 'how many', it was only with those peoples who took to agriculture that consistent and systematic number recording developed. Nomadic herdsmen developed the spoken language of number, but for them the need to retain numerical information was not sufficiently great to lead to the development of *systems* of written numerals. In the settled communities of those peoples who had become primarily cultivators, however, a different way of life developed from that of the herdsmen or the earlier wandering food hunters. Men paid taxes, trading grew, the calendar of course assumed even greater importance, and we can see that to these peoples the recording of numbers became a matter of some consequence. It was in these early civilizations that the first written number systems were evolved. It has been said that the first true written numbers were achieved when *spoken* number names and the *recorded* tally came together. Though all early written systems appear to have grown from simple tallying, the lines of development vary considerably in some respects. We must therefore refer separately to the numeral systems of some of the earlier civilizations.

Egyptian

Using ancient Egyptian numerals the number 39, for example, would be written

ΩΩΩ ‖‖‖

Such symbols were probably used fairly consistently as early as 3500 B.C.; even before that date the Egyptians had a calendar with twelve months of thirty days each, plus five feast days. Clearly the single stroke represents 'one' while the symbol Ω is a *collective symbol* which replaces ten of the unit strokes, just as in the previous chapter one of the second shepherd's fingers replaced ten of those of the first shepherd; i.e. the system was a decimal one. It has been suggested that the unit stroke originally represented a finger,

and that the symbol for ten came from the grouping of ten
unit strokes by an arc. There were eventually separate symbols for ten, a hundred, a thousand and all other powers of
ten up to ten million. Most of these symbols appear to have
represented particular objects. Thus the symbol for a thousand was a lotus plant, that for ten thousand a pointing
finger and, appropriately, that for a million an astonished
person.

These hieroglyphics were written on stone to record events,
and on wood and pottery; the Egyptians also used papyrus.
Papyrus was made by cutting the stem of a reed into thin
strips, laying the strips side by side on a board and then
placing another layer of strips across these. When these
were all soaked in water, pressed down and then allowed to
dry in the sun, the two layers stuck together. The surface
was then polished and a smooth writing surface produced.
The strips of papyrus were rolled up when not in use. Our
word 'paper' derives indirectly from the Egyptian papyrus.

The Egyptians wrote on the papyrus with a brush and
naturally the form of the number symbols varied considerably, just as the form of our letters written by hand do
to-day. The reader can illustrate this point for himself by
trying to copy the symbols shown on page 32. These symbols
should be regarded as no more than an attempt to represent,
on the printed page, the sort of symbols made by the Egyptians on stone, wood, pottery or papyrus. The way in which
the symbols were grouped is noteworthy. We do not find

IIIIIII for 7, but $\frac{IIII}{III}$, or possibly IIII III, a fact which re-

minds us of the limit to the size of a group which most
people can recognize at a glance. Lancelot Hogben in
Mathematics for the Million however puts forward a different explanation. He thinks that grouping in threes in this
system and those of other peoples was probably suggested
by the male organs of generation. The association of number and sex he suggests is not surprising for 'number script
was a by-product of an organized calendar, the need for
which came from man's preoccupation with his own

Ancient Egyptian Numerals

Hieroglyphics	Hieratic Symbols		Hieroglyphics	Hieratic Symbols
1		10		
2		20		
3		30		
4	or —	100	or	
5	or	1,000		
6		10,000		
7	or 2	100,000		
8		1,000,000		
9		10,000,000		

Examples of use of Hieroglyphics

32619

5162

fertility and that of his flocks.' Other writers have suggested that a tendency to group in threes was due in some cases to the earlier use of a system with three as base.

In rapid writing on papyrus, wood or pottery a cursive script developed from the hieroglyphics. This is now known as the hieratic script; a still later script, the demotic, developed from it, probably beginning in the seventh century B.C. On page 32 one of the varieties of hieratic numerals is shown. It is possible to see how they developed from the hieroglyphics but they represented a definite departure from the principle of the earlier numerals. The hieroglyphics might be described as *a tallying system* of numeration—the unit symbol and the higher collective symbols were repeated the appropriate number of times rather as tallies were laid out. On the other hand there was one single and distinct hieratic symbol to represent each number. The symbol gave hardly any suggestion of the number which it represented; we might therefore describe such a system as *a code system*. The development from simple tallying to a tallying system and then to a code system may be illustrated by the three ways of denoting 15:

simple tallying |||||||||||||||

tallying system   ∩ ⦀⦀

code system   ∧⏋

The development was one in which speed and compactness were gained, though a less direct picture was given of the number of things involved. Though Egyptian numerals were sometimes written with the highest powers of ten on the right I have in all examples in this chapter placed them to the left as in our own system.

Sumerian and Babylonian

In the first civilization in Mesopotamia the Sumerians had no papyrus, and stone was scarce; they may have written on leather, but their permanent records were made on clay, a material which played an important part in their lives. As they wrote on clay with a pointed stick their symbols were wedge-shaped; to-day we refer to them as *cuneiform* (from the Latin word 'cuneus', a wedge). After being written on the clay was baked hard in the sun or by fire. The Sumerian system of cuneiform numerals appears to be of similar age to that of the Egyptians. When later a Semitic people conquered the Sumerians and founded the Babylonian Empire they learnt the language and writing of the Sumerians, and to-day cuneiform writing is more frequently referred to as Babylonian than as Sumerian; the Assyrians and Chaldeans and other Semitic peoples also adopted the cuneiform numerals later. Thousands of clay tablets with cuneiform writing have been discovered, and many of them have been found to be mathematical texts or tables.

It is difficult, on a printed page, to depict marks made on clay. Bearing in mind this difficulty, the number 43 in Sumerian or Babylonian numerals might have been written as follows:

$$\langle\langle\langle\, \text{YYY}$$

Here symbols are used, as the Egyptian hieroglyphics were used, on a tallying system; the symbols to the left represent tens, those to the right units, and again symbols are grouped to avoid having too many in a row. For larger numbers a different principle was introduced. This can be seen in the following examples.

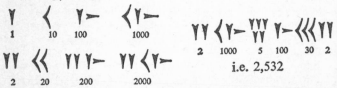

In the expressions for a thousand, two hundred and two thousand, values are *multiplied* when a symbol of lower value precedes one of higher value; in the reverse order they would, of course, be added. The expression for 2,532 involves both principles. The thousands and hundreds are expressed in unit symbols followed by the symbols for a thousand and a hundred; the symbols for a thousand and a hundred serve, as it were, as labels. The tens and units are expressed by the appropriate number of tens and units symbols.

Subtraction as well as multiplication was sometimes used in Babylonian numeration, but whereas multiplication was implied by the relative positions of the symbols, a definite sign Υ (lal) was used to indicate subtraction. Thus

$\langle\langle \Upsilon\rangle$ denoted 20–1 or 19.

Cuneiform numerals were not used only on the decimal system described above; there is in fact evidence of the use of systems with other bases in both Mesopotamia and Egypt. Here we shall only refer to the Babylonian sexagesimal system, i.e. a system with a base of 60. There have been various attempts to explain this use of 60. One explanation is that it was connected with an early belief that the year consisted of 360 days—12 lunar months each of 30 days. The influence of calendar reckoning on man's use of number has already been mentioned. We can see that dividing the apparent path of the sun round the earth into parts each corresponding to one of the 360 days would lead to our present 360 degrees in a revolution. It has been suggested that the Babylonians divided the 360 into six parts because they were familiar with the easy division of the circumference of a circle into six parts—perhaps with a rope on the sand. Another suggestion is that the earliest calendar of Mesopotamia was based on a zodiac of only six constellations, with the result that the year was divided into six periods of sixty days, each period being the time during which the sun remained in one of the zodiacal constellations. Several writers have expressed doubt about these explanations. They suggest that the division of the circle into 360 parts is more likely to be the result than the origin of the sexagesimal system and that the use of 60 may have arisen from a merger of two earlier systems with bases 6 and 10. Whatever the explanation, 60 was clearly an important number to the Babylonians. For example, each of the Babylonian gods was associated with one of the numbers up to 60, the number indicating the rank of the god in the heavenly hierarchy. To us, 60 may seem a surprisingly large number to use as a base, but we must remember that we are using this base when we write 5 hours 23 minutes 30 seconds or 22° 40′ 12″. These systems of time and angle measurement derive from the Greeks and were suggested to them by the Babylonian sexagesimal system.

An interesting example of the use of the base 60 is found on a Babylonian tablet of about 2000 B.C. The tablet contains a list of numbers. In the first seven of these the symbols for 1 and 10 are used on the tallying system to represent 1, 4, 9, 16, 25, 36 and 49—the squares of the numbers from 1 to 7. The list continues with symbols roughly as follows:

$$\text{Y} \ \underset{\smile}{\text{YYY}} \ ; \ \text{Y} \ \text{《Y} \ ; \ \text{Y} \ \text{《} \ ; \ \text{YY} \ \text{Y} \ ; \ \cdots\cdots$$

Taken as they stand they represent:

1   4   ;   1   21   ;   1   40   ;   2   1   ;   .....

The significance is not immediately obvious but if we take the first symbol of each group to denote the number of sixties and the second the number of units their values are seen to be:

$$1.60+4 \ ; \ 1.60+21 \ ; \ 1.60+40 \ ; \ 2.60+1 \ ; \ \cdots\cdots$$
i.e.   64   ;   81   ;   100;   121   ;   .....

These numbers continue the sequence of squares. We will discuss in the next chapter the reason why the Babylonians made tables of squares. The point of interest in the present connexion is that here the value of a symbol varied according to its *position* in relation to other symbols; in one position the symbol ' Y ' denoted 'one', in another position the collective unit 60, in another 3,600 (60 60s) and so on. It should be noted that though this system was sexagesimal it had a subsidiary base of 10; in writing numbers a tally symbol was used for ten as well as for one. In counting on this system the Babylonians counted in tens to sixty which they called a *soss*, then in sosses and smaller units to a *ner* which was ten sosses (i.e. 600), then in ners and smaller units to a *saru* which was six ners (i.e. 3,600).

The use of the principle of place value was a very important development in the method of writing numbers. With the value of a symbol varying according to its position it was unnecessary to have different symbols for each collective unit. The Babylonians had however only a limited appreciation of the principle and consequently their use of it was ambiguous in some cases. An example of this ambiguity is provided by a tablet found at Nippur in which, from the context, it appears that the symbols ' 〈𝖨𝖨 ' denote 720. The intention was thus to indicate twelve 60s, but there is nothing to show that the units are 60's. To make this clear a *Zero Symbol* should have been placed to indicate that there were no units. It was not, however, until about 200 B.C. that the Babylonians made any use of a symbol to denote the absence of a unit. The symbol which they then used for this purpose was **:** . Its use, however, was limited; it was used to indicate a gap between symbols, but not at the end of a number. Man came but slowly to the idea of using a symbol to denote the absence of something; young children to-day also find this idea difficult.

Maya and Aztec

The principle of place value was used more fully by the Maya of South Mexico and Central America. This ancient civilization of the American continent which developed independently of the civilizations of the Old World was mentioned in Chapter I as using a number system which was primarily vigesimal. In their written numerals there were obvious signs of the development from simple tallying.

They had a dot to represent one and a line for fives. The following examples illustrate the use of these two symbols for numbers less than 20.

Their method of denoting larger numbers showed clearly the influence of calendar making and time measurement. They proceeded on a scale of 20 with one deviation thus:

20 of the lowest units—kins (days) made 1 uinal
18 uinals made 1 tun (the Maya official year)
20 tuns made 1 katun
20 katuns made 1 cycle

and 20 cycles made 1 great cycle.

In writing large numbers the symbols were arranged vertically, those in the lowest place denoting units, the next 20s, the next 360s, and so on. Thus the symbols shown below represent the numbers we would write as 37,371 and 7,300.

The symbol roughly resembling a half-closed eye was the zero symbol; the Mayas used it to indicate the absence of any unit.

To illustrate this system our shepherds would have to use their toes as well as their fingers, though the second shepherd would have only eight toes and so call in the third shepherd after he had recorded eighteen 20s. There was some consistent use of a scale of 20 (i.e. counting in 1s, 20s, 400s, 8000s, etc.) but as Hogben puts it 'The most usual vulue of the successive orders seems to have been 1, 20, 360, 7,200 in accordance with their primitive social function rather than the more sophisticated advantages of rapid calculation'. From a mathematical point of view the desirability of a consistent scale seems obvious but in practical situations other considerations sometimes carry more weight. In the egg trade to-day, for example, the number of eggs is recorded by noting the number of long hundreds (120), the number of hands (6) and the number of single eggs; thus 3–5–4 denotes 394 eggs.

The Aztecs who lived in Mexico at a later period than the Mayas made a more consistent use of the scale of 20, but they did not use the principle of place value. The symbols they used were:

●	⊏	🌿	👛 (a purse)
1	20	400	8,000

The symbol for 400 meant 'numerous as hairs' while the bag or purse for 8,000 referred to the almost innumerable contents of a sack of cacao beans. Intermediate between the dot and the flag there was a lozenge-shaped symbol for 10, and the interval between 20 and 400 was ingeniously broken down as shown below.

100	200	300	400

It should be noted that 100 had not the significance for the Aztecs that it has for us. On our system it is a collective unit, on the Aztec it was merely equivalent to 5 of one unit or $\frac{1}{4}$ of another. The Aztec symbols were used on a tallying system; thus

represents 666.

It is interesting to note that the day was divided by the Aztecs into 20 parts and that a division of their army contained 8,000 soldiers (i.e. 20 × 20 × 20)

Chinese

Our knowledge of the beginnings of Chinese civilization is vague and uncertain. It seems probable that at an early period the Chinese carried out astronomical observations and developed some facility in the measurement of time and angles and in the use of fairly large numbers. It has been claimed that the oldest Chinese method of recording numbers was with knots in a string; the knotted cord was also used in other parts of the world, the best known probably being the Peruvian quipu. The Chinese numerals shown below form one of the oldest written number systems in the world, and they are still in regular use to-day. Though some business firms in China now use our numerals, others continue to use Chinese numerals in their accounts, and Chinese numerals are usually used on cheques. Naturally some of the symbols have changed in detail during many centuries of use, and the original significance of most of them is unknown. The first three symbols do, however, give a definite indication of a development from a simple tallying system; there may be some similarity between the evolution of the Chinese numerals and that of the Egyptian hieratic symbols.

Chinese Number Symbols   *Examples*

一	1	十	10	十三	13	四	
二	2	百	100	三十	30	萬	41,705
三	3	千	1,000	五十	50	千	
四	4	萬	10,000	五十三	53	七百	
五	5			百六	106	五	
六	6						
七	7						
八	8						
九	9						

There are separate code symbols for numbers from 1 to 10, and for 100, 1,000 and 10,000. The examples shown illustrate the principles on which symbols are combined. If we compare the symbols for 13 and 30 we see that when the 3 follows the 10 it is added, when placed above it is multiplied. The symbols for 53 show the application of both addition and multiplication; the group of symbols has the significance 'five tens and three' rather as if we were to write 5 T 3 where T denotes ten and serves as a label. The last example—41,705—illustrates the way in which larger numbers are represented. The same principles apply as for smaller numbers, the significance of the symbols being:

4 ten thousands, 1 thousand, 7 hundreds and 5

i.e. every second symbol serves as a label. It is interesting to note that the symbol for one is used to show that there is one thousand and that even without a zero symbol it is clear that there are no tens. We, of course, would not need a zero symbol to distinguish between 23, 203 and 230 if we wrote them as 2T3, 2H3, 2H3T—the idea is not, however, to be recommended. The method of representing numbers larger than 99,999 is similar; a million for example is written as 100 ten thousands. Other systems have also been used by the Chinese to represent numbers—for example, the system of numerals known as the Chinese Mercantile (or Merchant) Numerals, and also the rod numerals symbolism which we will consider in the next chapter; at one time a sexagesimal system may have been used.

With most peoples there developed, along with their increased facility with number, certain superstitions about numbers amounting almost to number worship in some cases. Even a brief account of Chinese numeration would not be complete without some reference to their mystical beliefs about numbers.

The Chinese magic square shown overleaf appears in the I-king (Book of Permutations) which was written before 1000 B.C. It represented patterns of black and white knots in strings; the white knots, symbolizing completeness,

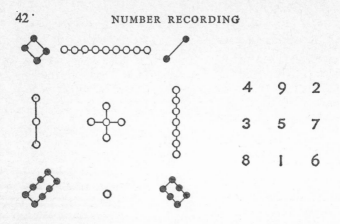

denoted the male or odd numbers and the black knots, symbolizing incompleteness, the female or even numbers. From the version given in our own symbols it can be seen that each of the first nine numbers was used once and that the sum of the three numbers in each row, column and diagonal was 15. These patterns were arranged by the Chinese on a holy board—the Lo-Shu—which was believed to have magical properties.

Number and sex were also associated in another way in the I-king when the two principles yang (—) the male, and ying (— —) the female, principles respectively of odd and even numbers, were combined to represent numbers. When three of these were used at a time the Pa-kua were formed.

Each of the Pa-kua was considered to hold the secret of one of the elements, and from a very early time they have been used for purposes of divination.

Indian

Few satisfactory records exist of early civilization in India and our knowledge of the written number systems used is very scanty. It would seem, however, that 2,000 or more years ago people in India, like other advanced peoples of that period, had some knowledge of astronomy and calculation. The earliest known examples of written numerals are found in the inscriptions of King Asoka, a great and peace-loving monarch who ruled a vast Indian empire in the third century B.C. The only number symbols found in these inscriptions are

$$| \qquad || \qquad + \qquad 6$$
$$1 \qquad 2 \qquad 4 \qquad 6$$

and various symbols for 50 and 200. In inscriptions of about a century later found on the walls of a cave of the Nānā Ghāt hill there are number symbols whose probable form was

$$- \quad = \quad \mp \quad 4 \quad 7 \quad ? \quad \propto \quad 0 \quad + \quad \varphi \quad \mathcal{H} \quad T$$
$$1 \quad 2 \quad 4 \quad 6 \quad 7 \quad 9 \quad 10 \quad 20 \quad 60 \quad 80 \quad 100 \quad 1,000$$

Symbols denoting 400, 700, 4,000, 6,000 and 20,000 are formed by placing the symbol for 100 or 1,000 followed by the appropriate units or tens symbol, thus $\mathcal{H}7$ denoted 700. A rather different set of numerals is found in the Saka inscriptions which are believed to date from the first century B.C.

$$| \quad || \quad ||| \quad X \quad IX \quad IIX \quad XX \quad 7 \quad 3 \quad 733 \quad \mathcal{X}1$$
$$1 \quad 2 \quad 3 \quad 4 \quad 5 \quad 6 \quad 8 \quad 10 \quad 20 \quad 50 \quad 100$$

In this system there are 'collective symbols' for 4, 10 and 20. The following numerals, probably of the first or second century A.D., are from the caves at Nasik.

$$- \quad = \quad \equiv \quad \Upsilon \quad \digamma \quad \zeta \quad 7 \quad \varsigma \quad ? \quad \propto \quad \ominus$$
$$1 \quad 2 \quad 3 \quad 4 \quad 5 \quad 6 \quad 7 \quad 8 \quad 9 \quad 10 \quad 20$$

There is considerable similarity between these and the Nānā Ghāt symbols. The first three of each clearly derive from tallying. The original significance of the others is uncertain. They may have been either the initial letters of the corresponding number words or the letters of the alphabet used in order—or their forms may have been suggested by the symbols used in some other countries. Such suggestions can only be tentative; there is no clear evidence to support these or more fanciful theories which have been put forward. It may be that the symbols were specifically designed to be used as numerals. In these systems there were probably separate symbols for units from 1 to 9, for multiples of ten from 10 to 90 and also symbols for 100 and 1,000 and sometimes for multiples of 100. Their use to denote, say, 642 would be comparable to our writing H6f2 where H and f are used as symbols for a hundred and forty respectively. The symbol for a hundred is used as a label as in the Chinese system but a single symbol is used for forty instead of symbols denoting ten and four. A later set of numerals known as the Devanagari numerals is shown here. They were used in India from about the eighth century A.D. It is not difficult to detect a resemblance between some of these symbols

१	२	३	४	५	६	७	८	९	०
1	2	3	4	5	6	7	8	9	0

and some of those from Nānā Ghāt and Nasik. But the Devanagari system differed from the earlier ones in that the principle of place value was used. This very important development in Hindu methods of writing numbers will be considered more fully in the last chapter.

Greek

The earliest known Greek records of numbers are in the form of upright strokes. In a record from Corinth for example, made in about the fifth century B.C., a fine of eight obols is written as IIIIIIII. In their developments from this form of tallying the Greeks may have been influenced by the number systems of the earlier civilizations, for by this time trade and commerce were resulting in greater contacts between peoples. Of the written number systems used in

Greece we can here consider only the two most important—
the Attic (or Herodianic) and the Alexandrian.

The Attic symbols, so called because they have been found
on several inscriptions in Athens, were probably used as
early as the sixth century B.C. though at that date large
numbers were frequently written in words. The Attic system
was a tallying system but, unlike the early Egyptian and
other tallying systems, its symbols were the initial letters of
the corresponding number words and there was a symbol
for 5 as well as for the multiples of 10.

Attic Greek Number Symbols

Symbol	I	Γ or Π	Δ	H	X	M
	1	5	10	100	1,000	10,000
Name	πέντε	δέκα	ἑκατόν	χίλιοι	μύριοι
	(penta-)	(deca-)	(hecto-)	(kilo-)	(myriad)

The use of a symbol for 5 probably derived from finger
counting. It was combined with other symbols to represent
other intermediate units 50, 500, 5,000 in the following way:

⟨Δ⟩	⟨H⟩	⟨X⟩
50	500	5,000

These combined symbols made it unnecessary to group symbols in two or more rows, since in no number was any one
symbol used more than four times.

Despite this device recording even small numbers sometimes required the writing of many symbols.

X ⟨H⟩HHHH⟨Δ⟩II representing 1952, involves
nine symbols; the reader may care to verify that 99 is
represented by ten symbols. It was probably this that led to
the use of another system—the Alexandrian system—from
the third century B.C. or earlier. This was a code system in
which the 24 letters of the Greek alphabet and 3 other
letters (Phoenician or obsolete Greek) were used.

Alexandrian Number Symbols

A	B	Γ	Δ	E	F	Z	H	Θ
1	2	3	4	5	6	7	8	9

I	K	Λ	M	N	Ξ	O	π	۹
10	20	30	40	50	60	70	80	90

P	ξ	T	Y	φ	X	Ψ	Ω	λ
100	200	300	400	500	600	700	800	900

An accent or a bar was sometimes placed above a letter to indicate that it was being used to represent a number.

For multiples of 1,000 a stroke was placed in front of the appropriate unit symbol—the stroke thus denoting multiplication by 1,000. Tens of thousands or myriads were indicated by an M with a units symbol above it, thus $\overset{\Gamma}{M}$ represented 30,000

We can make a simple comparison of the two systems by considering the following examples:

> Attic   *HHHΔΔΔIII*
>
> Alexandrian $\overline{TΛΓ}$
>
> 333

The Alexandrian example gives the more compact form but the Attic one gives a clearer picture of the structure of the number. The Alexandrian symbols give no indication, for example, that the numbers of hundreds, tens and units are the same. It should also be noted that in the Alexandrian system there were 27 symbols to be memorized as compared with 6 in the Attic system and 10 in ours. To the Greeks compactness apparently outweighed these disadvantages for the Alexandrian system eventually replaced all earlier systems, though Attic symbols were used for inscriptions and formal documents until a late date.

Roman

The Roman numerals are much better known to-day than any of the others referred to in this chapter. This fact is hardly to be attributed to any particular merit which they possessed, but rather to the extensive and comparatively recent influence of the Roman Empire. The Roman numerals formed another tallying system which differed from the Egyptian and Sumerian systems, as did the Attic Greek system, in having intermediate symbols for 5, 50 and 500. In this respect it differed too from the system of Roman number words—the word the Romans used for sixteen for example meant 'ten and six'; the symbol they wrote XVI meant 'ten and five and one'.

The Romans are generally supposed to have taken over their numerals from the Etruscans. The Etruscans, who possibly came from Asia Minor, ruled in Italy north of the Tiber perhaps as early as 1000 B.C. and are thought to have conquered Rome in the seventh century B.C. They were a civilized people compared with the Latin tribes living to the south of the Tiber; they appear to have been influenced by eastern Mediterranean or Aegean civilizations. These may have had some effect on their development of a written number system. When the Etruscans were driven out of Rome in about 500 B.C. many of their customs were naturally retained.

Much has been written about the original significance of the Roman numerals. The present form of the Roman numerals is shown below and with these some earlier forms used in Etruscan and Roman times.

Roman Numerals

Earlier forms	I	V, Λ	X, +	Ψ, ⊥, ↓, ⊥	⊗, ⊕, ⊖	D, D	Φ, ↀ, CD
Present form	I	V	X	L	C	D	M
	1	5	10	50	100	500	1,000

As far as the origin of the symbols for five and ten are concerned two schools of thought deserve attention. The first
considers V to have been a representation of the open hand
with the fingers closed together and the thumb held apart.
The symbol X is then considered to have represented two
crossed hands or a double V.

The alternative explanation is that X came from crossing
off a row of ten strokes thus:

(just as the Egyptian symbol ∩ may have come from bracket-
ing ten strokes), and that V for 5 followed naturally, being the
top half of X. In support of this explanation it is pointed out
that 5 was also sometimes represented on early Roman
monuments by Λ, which may be described as the bottom
half of X.

C and M are believed to be late forms of the symbols for
100 and 1,000—forms which were probably adopted because
they are the initial letters of the number words 'centum'
(100) and 'mille' (1,000). C is considered to have developed
from the symbol Θ (theta) though no intermediate forms
have yet been discovered. The symbols CI and I⊃ being half
of CI⊃ came to represent 500 and led to the later adoption
of D. In a similar way L is said to have originated from the
bisection of a form of the symbol for 100; an alternative
theory is that it derived from an early form ↓ of the Greek
aspirate 'chi'.

The intermediate symbols for 5, 50 and 500 enabled numbers to be written more compactly than on a purely decimal
tallying system. Another device which economized in space
was the subtraction of values when a lesser symbol was
placed to the left of one of larger value; examples of this are
the familiar IV and IX for 4 and 9. Both devices constituted
a departure from the simple pattern of the number system,
and probably made it more difficult in later times for those
accustomed to the Roman system to take to the modern
system with the principle of place value.

Apart from the occasional use of the subtraction device, Roman numerals were used on the ordinary tallying system for numbers less than ten thousand. In writing larger numbers various methods were used. CCIƆƆ and CCCIƆƆƆ for 10,000 and 100,000 developed from CIƆ for 1,000, and sometimes these symbols were repeated a large number of times in denoting multiples of 10,000 and 100,000. IƆƆ and IƆƆƆ being halves of these symbols were used to represent 5,000 and 50,000. Some methods used to denote large numbers involved multiplication. Thus in CXM for 110,000 or XIIM for 12,000 the smaller number was understood to multiply the larger, though in such cases M may have been looked on as an abbreviation for the word 'milia' rather than as a number symbol. Occasionally in late Roman times a bar was placed over a letter to increase its value a thousand fold, as in $\overline{\text{CXX}}$ for 120,000.

General Principles.

Though the above survey of numeral systems covers only a selection of those known it should serve to illustrate the variety of methods and devices used by different peoples in recording numbers. Broadly the systems may be classified according to:

(1) whether they used tally or code symbols
(2) whether they applied the principle of place value
(3) their base.

Tally symbols provided a simple way of representing numbers. Their use gave direct expression to the idea of a collective unit and most early peoples appear to have used tally symbols when they first developed a written number system. Some peoples continued to use tally symbols throughout their history, and some, e.g. the Romans, used them throughout without the principle of place value. But many came later to use code symbols. The Greeks made this change deliberately but in most cases the code system evolved gradually from the tallying system. The Egyptian hieratic symbols came from the rapid writing of the hieroglyphics, the first three symbols in the Chinese system suggest an earlier tallying system and it is possible that with other peoples $=$ and $\equiv$ changed to Z and $\tilde{Z}$ and hence to such forms as our 2 and 3 while II and III became Γ and $\Gamma^\sim$ and later, for example, the Arabic υ and μ. A code system is compact to write but it involves more different symbols than a tallying system and makes heavy demands on the memory, particularly if the principle of place value is not applied. These and other points are illustrated by the following comparison of the positions of our shepherds' fingers with various ways of writing the numbers that they are recording.

SHEPHERDS' FINGERS recording four hundreds and twenty-seven

3rd shepherd   2nd shepherd   1st shepherd

TALLY SYMBOLS used to record this number

(a) *without the principle of place value* (e.g. Egyptian hieroglyphics)

$$9999 \qquad \cap\cap \qquad |||||||$$

i.e. different symbols to represent hundreds, tens and units.

(b) *on the principle of place value*

$$|||| \qquad || \qquad |||||||$$

i.e. same symbol used throughout; the position of a symbol indicates its value.

(c) *with labels*

$$||||h \qquad ||t \qquad |||||||$$

The labels h and t (hundreds and tens) make the value of a symbol clearer to those who do not fully appreciate the general pattern of the number system, but are an encumbrance in other ways.

(d) *with devices to save space*

> **CD   XX   VII**

instead of

> **CCCC   XX   IIIIIII**

i.e. *intermediate symbol* V instead of 11111

and *subtraction* of C from D instead of addition of CCCC

(this subtraction device is in line with the expressions 'all of the fingers all but done with' and 'fold down one' for 4 and 9, and with the modern 'ten to five' for '4.50').

CODE SYMBOLS used to record the same number

(a) *without the principle of place value*

Different sets of symbols are used for each decimal order as though the fact that each finger is different is recognized by giving each a different symbol

3rd shepherd   2nd shepherd   1st shepherd

and the number recorded by noting the last finger raised by each shepherd.

> V   K   G

(b) *with the principle of place value*

The same set of symbols is used for each decimal order and for each shepherd's fingers

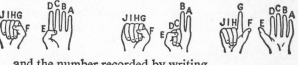

and the number recorded by writing

> D   B   G

i.e. the positions of the symbols D, B and G indicate that they refer respectively to hundreds, tens and units.

(c) *with labels*

          Dh   Bt   G

The Chinese system is of this type.

As we saw when considering the Babylonian systems, tally
symbols used with the principle of place value lead to
ambiguity in the writing of certain numbers. We can write
four hundred and seven, for example, as

9999   **|||| |||**

but if we write

          |||| **|||| |||**

the symbols may well be taken to denote forty-seven. Similarly, with code symbols

          V   G

clearly denotes four hundred and seven since V represents
'four hundreds', but

          D   G

does not, since D represents 'four' and here indicates that
there are four of some unit—probably tens. To write four
hundred and seven when the principle of place value is
applied there must be some means of indicating that there
are no tens. We have already considered the limited use of a
symbol for this purpose by the Babylonians and the fuller
use by the Maya; in the last chapter we will consider the
origin of our zero symbol which is, of course, used with code
symbols. With a symbol to denote an empty gap and nine
other code symbols used on the principle of place value, it
is possible to represent any number; such a system, as we
will see, also makes possible the development of written
methods of calculation.

In the above illustrations I have followed the Greeks in
using the letters of the alphabet as code symbols though for
convenience I have used our alphabet. From some points
of view the letters of the alphabet form quite suitable

number symbols—they are clearly distinguishable from one another and we all know the order in which they are used. Their use, however, has the disadvantage that words and numbers may become confused and in some cases, particularly with the Greek and Hebrew systems, it led to a form of number supersitition known as Gematria. In Gematria, the 'number of a word' was found by adding the numbers which the letters of the word represented; this number was then used to make predictions or to assess merit—the superiority of Achilles over Hector was, for example, attributed to the fact that in Greek numerals the numbers of their names were respectively 1,276 and 1,225. In Revelation (xiii, 18) we have, ' Here is wisdom. Let him that hath understanding count the number of the beast: for it is the number of a man; and his number is Six hundred three score and six.' This 'number of the beast' has been much used in theological feuds. It appears to have been a master stroke, particularly at the time of the Reformation, to write an opponent's name in such a way that it could be proved equivalent to 666 and much effort was spent in doing this. The number was, for example, assigned to Luther, to various Popes and to Mohammed; some readers may remember, from Tolstoy's *War and Peace*, that 'L'Empereur Napoléon' can also be made equivalent to 'the number of the beast'.

THE BASE OF A SYSTEM may be illustrated by considering not the way in which the shepherds' fingers are recorded, but the number of fingers or their equivalent which each member of the counting team has, i.e. the size of the collective units; to illustrate the use of a system with sixty as base, we would need creatures with sixty fingers each. In the examples below the number four hundred and twenty-seven is first analysed in terms of the different collective units—the units which the different members of the counting team would be recording; it is then written down using the given base in

(a) a tallying system with only a unit symbol,
(b) a code system with our number symbols.

In both cases the principle of place value is employed.

Base sixty—counting ones, sixties, three thousand six hundreds, etc.

Four hundred and twenty-seven = 7 sixties + 7 over.
Written (a) |||| |||| (b) **77**
       ||| |||

Base twenty—counting ones, twenties, four hundreds (i.e. twenty twenties) etc.

Four hundred and = 1 four hundred + 1 twenty + 7
twenty-seven   over
Written (a) | | |||| (b) **117**
           |||

Base ten—counting ones, tens, hundreds, etc.

Four hundred and = 4 hundreds + 2 tens + 7 over.
twenty-seven
Written (a) |||| || |||| (b) **427**
              |||

Base five—counting ones, fives, twenty-fives, one hundred and twenty-fives, etc.

Four hundred and = 3 one hundred and twenty-fives
twenty-seven   + 2 twenty-fives + 0 fives + 2
            ones.
Written (a) ||| || . || (b) **3202**

Base two—counting ones, twos, fours, eights, etc.

Four hundred and = 1(256) + 1(128) + 0(64) + 1(32)
twenty-seven   + 0(16) + 1(8) + 0(4) + 1(2)
            + 1(1)

(here symbols in brackets are used instead of words because of the large number of units involved.)

Written (a) || . | . | . || (b) **110101011**

A system with as large a base as sixty, or even twenty, would clearly be inconvenient to use—on a tallying system it would often involve writing very many strokes, and on a code system there would be fifty-nine different symbols to learn. At the other extreme a system with a base of two, or even five, involves recording many different collective units for quite a small number. Some base between these extremes is to be preferred. We use 10 because of our heritage of finger counting. It would be difficult to change this custom though 8 or 12, having more convenient factors, would have some advantages.

Knots and Notches

This chapter on number recording has been concerned mainly with written numerals. Though the written form is the most important of man's methods of recording number it is not the only one that he has used; among other known devices are knotted strings and tally sticks. The knotted string has already been mentioned in connexion with Chinese numeration, and the device was used in many other parts of the world. Herodotus tells of the King of Persia handing the Ionians a thong with 60 knots as a calendar for 2 months. In each city in Peru there was an 'official of the knots' who used the quipu, the Peruvian knotted cord, to keep the city's accounts. In India, in more recent times (1872), some of the Santál headmen, being unable to write, made knots in cords of four different colours when taking the census; a knot in a black cord denoted a man, and in a red cord a woman, while white and yellow cords were used for boys and girls. Tally sticks—sticks in which notches were cut to record numbers—were used in ancient Egypt and later in most European countries. The English tally stick for recording money had different sized notches for pence, shillings, pounds, ten pounds, etc. When a loan was made, the appropriate notches were cut, the stick split in two so that each part was notched and one part kept by the borrower and the other by the lender. The British Exchequer used tally sticks from the twelfth century onwards, the pieces being of unequal size—the thinner piece, the 'foil', was retained as a record of payment, the main piece, the 'stock', served as a receipt for the payer or 'stockholder'. Conservatism kept this system in official use long after the introduction of modern numerals made it unnecessary; it was finally given up early in the nineteenth century. A similar device was used at one time by the tallyman in the Kentish hopfields.

CHAPTER III

EARLY CALCULATING DEVICES

WHEN a calculation is too difficult for us to do mentally we resort to pencil and paper and do it with our number symbols. This is, however, a comparatively recent innovation. The systems of number symbols described in the previous chapter developed as a means of recording numbers and not as a means of carrying out calculations. In any case, papyrus, parchment and earlier types of paper would have been much too scarce and expensive to be used for jotting down calculations. Paper was probably made in China before the birth of Christ, but it was the thirteenth or fourteenth century before paper-making spread to Europe, and cheap paper from pulp is a product of the nineteenth century.

In the early civilizations, before the invention of money, there was not much need for calculation. Problems no doubt arose in barter and trade, in the levying of taxes, in calendar making and in military organization, which made some form of calculation necessary, but for most people numerical problems seldom required much more than counting and recording. Even in Roman times, calculations arose much less frequently than they do to-day in our urban industrial civilization.

Until only a few hundred years ago few people could carry out more than the most simple calculations. The most common method of carrying out simple calculations was to use the fingers. Simple addition follows naturally from finger tallying—one counts off three fingers and then the next four and so adds three and four. But more complicated methods were devised; we have also seen that more elaborate methods of denoting numbers with the fingers were commonly used. Finger reckoning was taught in Roman schools and, according to Quintilian, anyone was thought to be imperfectly trained in arithmetic if he betrayed 'by an uncertain or awkward movement of his fingers, a want of confidence in his calculations'. Finger methods were even devised for multiplying and dividing, though these were not common in Western Europe. There was an interesting method, possibly of Roman origin, for multiplying numbers greater than 5. To multiply 8 by 9 by this method three fingers on one hand and four fingers on the other were raised, these representing respectively 6, 7, 8, and 6, 7, 8, 9, i.e. the numerals over 5. The product was then found as follows. The tens digit was obtained by counting the total number of fingers raised— 7 in this case—while the units digit was given by the product of the numbers of fingers not raised—in this case 2 and 1. The reader may care to verify that this simple device works for the products of any pair of numbers between 5 and 10. The connexion between the product of the two numbers and the result of the procedure described is by no means an obvious one; it is fairly easy, using modern algebraic notation, to *verify* the relationship but one wonders how it was originally discovered. The fact that 8 is 3 more than 5 and 2 less than 10 is, of course, frequently apparent to anyone counting on the fingers, and we have seen in primitive number words how these facts tend to impress themselves on the mind. This may explain how the 3 and 4 and the 2 and 1 were associated with 8 and 9, but still leaves us guessing as to how their combination to give 72 originated. The chief advantage of this device was that with a knowledge only of products up to 5×5 it was possible to obtain any product up to 10×10. This and similar devices were used in widely different places and in some continued in use until very recent times. We will see later that the same principle was also applied sometimes in written arithmetic.

In the earlier civilizations calculation was usually considered to be a complicated and almost supernatural process. Calculations were carried out by experts who were regarded with great awe; in many civilizations these experts were the priests. One wonders if there is any connexion between this earlier attitude to calculation and the feelings which mathematics seem to arouse in many minds to-day.

The professional calculators of earlier civilizations did not use written methods to carry out their calculations; indeed it would have been difficult to devise written methods with the number symbols which they used. It is not difficult to see that the addition of

$$\text{999 ∩∩∩ III} \quad \text{and} \quad \text{9 ∩∩∩ II} \quad \text{gives} \quad \text{999 ∩∩ III}$$

for this only involves the putting together of like symbols with appropriate replacements by higher symbols; and the subtraction of numbers expressed in tallying symbols is similarly straightforward. But the multiplication and division of numbers so expressed can hardly be contemplated; the multiplication of

$$\text{999 ∩∩∩ III} \quad \text{by} \quad \text{9 ∩∩∩ II}$$

would clearly be an elaborate procedure.

Multiplication and division require the use of number relationships and these are difficult to apply symbolically unless each number is expressed by a single symbol. With code symbols, methods nearer to modern calculation are possible but a system like the Alexandrian system with a different set of symbols for each decimal order would involve many number relationships. For example, if we compare the multiplication of 34 by 22 set out in (a) using modern numerals and in (b) using the letters of our alphabet on the Alexandrian pattern we see that in (a) the number relationships $2 \times 4 = 8, 2 \times 3 = 6, 6 + 8 = 14, 6 + 1 = 7$ are involved whereas (b) involves $B \times D = H, B \times L = O,$ $K \times D = Q, K \times L = X, Q + O = SM, S + X = Y.$

The relationship $B \times D = H$ $(2 \times 4 = 8)$ does not help at all in $K \times D = Q$ $(20 \times 4 = 80)$.

	(a)	34		(b)	LD
		22			KB
		68			OH
		68			XQ
		748			YMH

Even in addition complications arise when code symbols are used without the principle of place value. In the following pairs of statements

(i) $|| + || = ||||$ (ii) $B + B = D$ (iii) $B + B = D$
   $\Omega\Omega + \Omega\Omega = \Omega\Omega\Omega\Omega$ $K + K = M$ $B \cdot + B \cdot = D \cdot$
                                          (where $\cdot$ denotes
                                             an empty gap)

the parallel between $2 + 2 = 4$ and $20 + 20 = 40$ is clear in (i) with tally symbols and (iii) with code symbols used on the principle of place value, and in (iii) the relationships are expressed concisely. But in (ii) with code symbols used without the principle of place value the parallel is completely hidden. Such a system shows how in mathematics a symbolism can be a hindrance if there is too much of it.

The Counting Board

The expert calculators of earlier civilization carried out their calculations with the aid of a device which we call an abacus or counting board, and which grew from man's use of tallies. The essential feature of all abaci was that tallies or counters could be placed in or moved along a series of parallel rows; the basic principle in their use by peoples with a decimal number system was that ten counters in one row were equivalent to one counter in the next row. Such devices to aid the systematic use of tallies in calculation were used in widely separate parts of the world; the idea probably originated in several different centres, and its value in commerce led to its being carried to other regions by merchants and traders. The abacus is believed to have been used in ancient Egypt and Babylon, and was an essential feature in calculation in nearly all subsequent civilizations. The practical details of the abacus have varied considerably in different places and at different times. In one type, marks which could be easily erased served as counters; the ancient Hindus, for example, used the dust-board, or sand-tray, which was common also in the Greek and Roman civilizations. It is incidentally interesting to note that a sand-tray was used by Euclid when drawing geometrical figures. Tablets smeared with wax in which marks could be made by scratching with a stylus were also used in Greece and Rome and were in use in Europe in the Middle Ages. Some writers trace the origin of the word abacus to the Semitic 'abac' meaning 'dust'; others think the Greek 'abax', meaning 'tablet', a more probable source.

Another type of abacus, probably used by most people who developed any form of abacus, was the ruled board or slab on which loose counters were placed. Our word 'calculate' itself derives from the Latin 'calculus' meaning pebble or small piece of marble. A Jesuit priest writing in the sixteenth century refers to the Peruvians' use of kernels of wheat. 'In order to effect a difficult computation for which an able calculator would require pen and ink—these Indians made use of their kernels of wheat. They place one here, three somewhere else and eight I know not where. They move one kernel here and three there and the fact is that they are able to complete their computation without making the smallest mistake.'

In a third type of abacus the counters were attached and could only move along their own rows—in some pierced balls moved along parallel rods, in others buttons moved in grooves. This type was used in many parts of the world—as examples we have the Chinese *suan-pan*, the Japanese *soroban*, the Russian *s'choty*, the Turkish *coulba* and the Armenian *choreb* some of which are still in use to-day.

In all forms of the abacus we see the value of a counter varying with its *position*. In fact the abacus might be described as an instrument for giving expression to the principle of place value. A few simple examples should make the use of the abacus clear. In these examples the questions and answers are given in modern numerals but clearly the methods would be equally applicable to questions expressed in any other decimal notation, as such notations necessarily indicate the number of units, tens, hundreds, thousands, etc. It should also be noted that questions given in number words are dealt with as readily as those expressed in symbols. The diagrams given below are intended to indicate method rather than to depict practical details; the dots shown each represent one counter. Some readers may prefer to construct their own dust-tray, ruled board with counters, or bead-frame, and perform the calculations for themselves.

1. Add 531 and 126

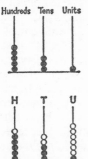

Here counters are set out to represent the number 5 3 1.

To each row in turn the appropriate number of counters to represent 1 2 6 have been added. The number of counters in each row is now counted—there are 6 in the hundreds row, 5 in the tens and 7 in the units—hence the result 657.

(In the above diagrams the first number is represented by black counters and second number by white counters—in practice of course all counters would be the same.)

2. Add 1248 and 805

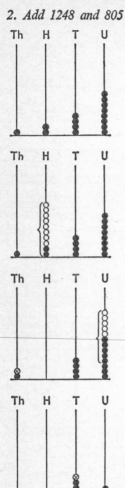

These black counters represent 1248.

Eight counters (the hundreds of 805) have been added to the hundreds row, making 10 counters in this row.

The ten counters from the hundreds row have all been removed and replaced by one counter (×) in the thousands row. Five counters (the units of 805) have been added to the units row.

As there were thus 13 counters in the units row 10 of these have been removed and replaced by one counter (×) in the tens row.
The final result is seen to be 2,053.

This example illustrates the replacement of ten counters by one counter in the next row; it is the only complication which arises in addition. (In the above diagrams the counter which replaces 10 is marked with a cross, though again in practice all counters would be the same.)

3. Subtract 251 from 685

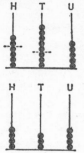

This shows counters to represent 685 with dotted lines indicating the counters to be removed.

After their removal the result is seen to be 434.

4. Subtract 263 from 537

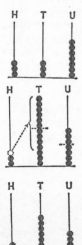

Here counters are set out to represent 537, the dotted line showing those to be removed from the hundreds row.

This shows the position after their removal. It is not possible to remove 6 counters from the tens row.

Accordingly 1 counter in the hundreds row is replaced by 10 in the tens row.

It is then possible to remove 6 counters from the tens row. After also removing 3 counters from the units row the result is seen to be 274.

This procedure is equivalent to what is known as the de-composition method of subtraction—a method which is to be preferred to others as far as aiding the understanding of our number system is concerned.

It is worth noting that in using the abacus for addition or subtraction it does not matter whether one begins at the right or the left end. Thus in Example *4* we began with 537 and our successive remainders were 337, 277 and 274. As no writing was done until the final result was obtained, no inconvenience was caused by the number of hundreds changing twice.

The methods described above treat addition and subtraction as the mere putting together and taking away of counters, followed by counting. They are in fact *counting* board operations requiring no more facility with number than the ability to count. As Rouse Ball puts it, the abacus enabled 'the ancients to add and subtract without any knowledge of theoretical arithmetic'. One imagines, however, that anyone using an abacus frequently would learn to make short cuts in the procedure described. An experienced calculator would hardly lay out 13 counters in the units column in Example *2*. Having placed 9 there he would probably place the next one in the tens row, remove the 9 and then put down the re-maining 3; in some forms of abacus it is not possible in any case to use more than 9 counters in any one row. And as with experience he became aware of more and more number bonds, he would be less dependent on the tedious counting out of counters. When, for example, he knew that 5 and 8 make 13 he would deal with the units in Example *2* by immediately placing 1 more counter in the tens row and leaving 3 in the units row. It seems that when this stage of proficiency was reached there often arose a disinclination to count out even as many as 9 counters and as a result, we find in some forms of the abacus a device for indicating 5, 50, 500, etc., by using only one counter. This *intermediate replacement*, on the abacus, corresponds, of course, to the use, in writing, of a symbol to represent an intermediate unit.

Devices for Intermediate Replacement

It is interesting to consider some of the ways in which intermediate replacement was carried out. The following examples—the Greek counting board, the Roman bronze abacus and the Chinese counting rods—illustrate three different methods.

The only Greek counting board discovered is a marble slab about 5 feet by 2 feet 6 inches. It has ruled on it a group of eleven parallel lines with crosses on the third, sixth and ninth and, set apart from this group, another parallel group of six lines for fractions. The numerals engraved on it are Attic symbols. Counters placed *on* the first group of lines represented units and powers of 10; counters placed *between* these lines represented 5s, 50s, 500s, etc. Here, then, the intermediate unit was denoted by using the space between the lines. The same idea was used in the counting boards common in Europe in the Middle Ages. The ruled table, or

Diagram of Counting Board used in Europe in the Middle Ages

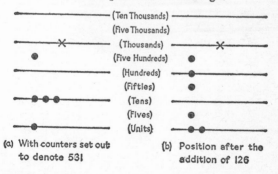

(a) With counters set out to denote 531

(b) Position after the addition of 126

'line abacus', became the most popular form in Western Europe; in many places it was still almost the only means of calculation in commerce as late as the fifteenth century. In it, crosses to aid the eye were placed on the thousands line and on the millions line with boards that extended that far. It was this practice that led to our use of commas when writing numbers.

The Roman bronze abacus was of the type in which the counters were able to move only in their own grooves; counters were 'out of action' when left at the bottom of their grooves and only those moved to the top were taken into account. The seven longer grooves to the left in the example shown were used to denote units, tens, hundreds, etc., the higher powers of ten being to the left. The shorter upper grooves were used to represent the intermediate units five, fifty, five hundred, etc., a counter in an upper groove thus representing five of the counters in the corresponding lower groove. The combined use of the upper and lower grooves made it possible to represent any number up to ten million. As we shall see shortly, a similar method for representing intermediate units was used in the Chinese *suan-pan* and the Japanese *soroban*. The five grooves to the right of the Roman abacus were for fractions—$\frac{1}{2}$s, $\frac{1}{12}$ths, $\frac{1}{24}$ths, $\frac{1}{48}$ths, $\frac{1}{72}$nds.

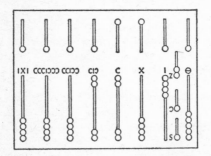

Roman Bronze Abacus with counters denoting 2754.

With the Chinese counting rods, which were used for calculating before 500 B.C., the value denoted by a rod depended not only on the column in which it was placed, but also on whether it lay along or across the column.

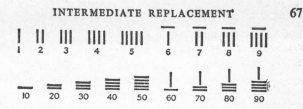

From the above illustration it can be seen that in representing units greater than 5 a rod placed across the column denoted 5 and for multiples of 10 greater than 50 a rod lying up and down the column denoted 50. The method of expressing units was repeated in the hundreds column and that for tens in the thousands column. Thus 3 8 7 2 was represented by

$$\equiv \quad \overline{\overline{\text{III}}} \quad \underline{\underline{\text{I}}} \quad \text{II}$$

Chinese counting rods were usually made of bamboo but other materials were also used. An emperor in the sixth century A.D. had counting rods cast in iron for the use of his people; 'reckoning with ivory rods' is still used as an allusion to wealth. The Koreans, who adopted the plan from the Chinese, used counting rods, usually made of bone, until quite recently.

Counting rods continued generally in use in China until the thirteenth century and written numerals which developed from the counting rods and which eventually included a zero symbol 0 were in use in China as late as the nineteenth century. The *suan-pan* was a later development in China and probably first appeared in the twelfth century. It was similar to the Roman grooved abacus except that, instead of buttons moving along grooves, it had pierced balls moving along slender bamboo rods. The instrument shown in the accompanying diagram has five balls on each lower rod and two on each upper rod. Balls were

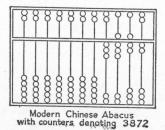

Modern Chinese Abacus
with counters denoting 3872

only 'in action' when moved to the middle bar. The Japanese form of the *suan-pan*, known as the *soroban*, is similar except that it has only one ball on each upper rod. In both the *suan-pan* and the *soroban* we have again counters in the upper rows replacing five of those in the corresponding lower row.

Each of the three methods of representing intermediate units made it unnecessary for a skilled calculator ever to place more than 4 or 5 counters in any one row. This made it possible for the number of counters in any row to be seen at a glance. Against this advantage we must set the disadvantages that more exchanges had to be made, and two different 'rates of exchange' were involved—5 lowers replaced by 1 upper, and 2 uppers replaced by 1 lower to the left, instead of all on a 10 for 1 basis. This complication and the fact that numbers could not be set out in full could be a serious handicap to the unskilled. To those, however, who were familiar with number bonds, and who did not rely on mere counting in addition and subtraction, a device for representing intermediate units was a great boon. It has been said that Japanese experts can add and subtract more rapidly with the *soroban* than we can with pencil and paper. They have the dexterity of an expert typist; in adding they add each number on to what is already recorded and are able to do this as rapidly as the numbers are read out to them.

Methods of Multiplication and Division

As far as addition and subtraction are concerned, the abacus is a very convenient instrument, but when multiplication and division are involved it is by no means so useful. Our knowledge of the methods of multiplying and dividing used by the ancients is far from complete. In considering the methods which they used it is important to realize that the ideas of multiplication and division, as we think of them to-day, grew only gradually. Problems which we would solve by multiplication or division can be solved by repeated addition or subtraction, and many peoples appear to have used such methods, performing the addition or subtraction on the abacus. To take a simple example, we would, if we knew that there were 24 buttons on a card, find the number on 6 cards by finding

$$6 \times 24.$$

The result could, however, be obtained by finding

$$24 + 24 + 24 + 24 + 24 + 24.$$

Similarly if we wished to know how many cards to buy to obtain 100 buttons we would work out

$$100 \div 24.$$

The answer could be obtained though by taking

24 from 100 leaving 76
24 from 76 leaving 52
24 from 52 leaving 28
24 from 28 leaving 4.

This shows clearly that we need 4 complete cards and 4 more buttons from a fifth card.

Repeated addition and subtraction were, to earlier calculators, natural even if lengthy ways of solving particular numerical problems, and we must remember that calculation was carried out to solve actual problems and not to obtain answers to examples in a textbook. As late as the tenth century A.D., 5 400s were calculated in a mathematical work by addition, and the same writer when dividing 6152 by 15 tried all the multiples of 15 until he found that 400 15s gave him 6000; this left a remainder 152 and he began again and found that 10 15s gave 150. He thus had a final answer of 410 with a remainder 2. His method could more suitably be described as 'trial multiplication' than as division.

It is obvious that repeated addition would be very tedious if a large number of things were to be added. The Ahmes Papyrus, a document from which we learn much about Egyptian mathematics of more than 3,000 years ago, shows an improved method which involved *doubling* and adding.

It is as if to find the number of buttons on 13 cards we proceeded as follows:

> 1 card has 24 buttons
> 2 cards have 48 buttons
> 4 cards have 96 buttons
> 8 cards have 192 buttons

13 cards = 8 cards + 4 cards + 1 card

∴ 13 cards have 192 + 96 + 24 buttons = 312 buttons.

Both the doubling and the final addition could be performed
on the abacus, and the Egyptian numerals were quite ade-
quate to record the results of doubling, if necessary, until
they were added.

This doubling method often referred to as 'duplation',
was frequently used on the abacus by the Egyptians and by
other ancient peoples. Even in the Middle Ages when
modern numerals were coming into use, multiplication was
still often carried out in this way, though tables were probably used to aid doubling.

In the above illustration of duplation 13 was expressed as
the sum of various powers of 2. As any whole number can
be expressed in this way any multiplication can be performed
by duplation though the process may be lengthy—it does,
however, require the use of only the two-times table.

In some cases it was found easier to follow the doubling
with subtraction instead of addition. To illustrate this, we
could, in finding the buttons on fourteen cards, take the
doubling one step further to

16 cards have 384 buttons

and then as 14 cards = 16 cards − 2 cards,

we see that 14 cards have 384−48 buttons=336 buttons.

While considering duplation it is perhaps appropriate to
digress to refer to what is often called Russian multiplication—a method which involves doubling, halving and
adding. To use this method to multiply 21 by 23 the two
numbers are written side by side as shown.

21	23
10	~~46~~
5	92
2	~~184~~
1	368
	————
	483

The numbers under the 21 are obtained by repeated halving, ignoring $\frac{1}{2}$s, until the value 1 is obtained; the numbers under the 23 are obtained by doubling the same number of times. Any numbers in the second row which are opposite even numbers in the first row are then crossed out and the sum of the remainder is the required answer. This may seem a peculiar procedure, but if we note that

$$21 = 10 \text{ 2s and } 1 \text{ 1}$$
$$10 \text{ 2s} = 5 \text{ 4s and } 0 \text{ 2s}$$
$$5 \text{ 4s} = 2 \text{ 8s and } 1 \text{ 4}$$
$$2 \text{ 8s} = 1 \text{ 16 and } 0 \text{ 8s}$$

i.e., that $21 = 1 \quad 1 + 0 \quad 2s + 1 \quad 4 + 0 \quad 8s + 1 \quad 16$ we see that when multiplying 23 by 21 we need to take $1 \quad 23 + 0 \quad 46s + 1 \quad 92 + 0 \quad 184s + 1 \quad 368$.
The method shown may then be regarded as an abbreviation of

$$21 \times 23 = 10 \times 46 + 1 \times 23$$
$$10 \times 46 = 5 \times 92 + 0 \times 46$$
$$5 \times 92 = 2 \times 184 + 1 \times 92$$
$$2 \times 184 = 1 \times 368 + 0 \times 184$$
$$1 \times 368 = \qquad 1 \times 368$$
$$\overline{\qquad 483 \qquad}$$

In this we can see the connexion between odd and even numbers in the left column and the numbers in the right column.

Other methods of multiplication used by early calculators involved the use of tables of squares as well as the abacus— as we have seen, the Babylonians compiled such tables. We may illustrate two of these methods by setting out, in modern numerals, the multiplication of 24×14:

(1)

$24\ 14s = 14\ 14s$ and $10\ 14s$

$\qquad = 14\ 14s$ and $10\ 10s$ and $10\ 4s$

$\qquad = 14\ 14s$ and $10\ 10s$ and $4\ 4s$ and $6\ 4s$

$\qquad = 14\ 14s$ and $10\ 10s$ and $4\ 4s$ and $4\ 4s$ and $2\ 4s$

$\qquad = 14\ 14s$ and $10\ 10s$ and $4\ 4s$ and $4\ 4s$ and $2\ 2s$ and $2\ 2s$

All these values could be obtained from the table of squares and the results added on the abacus. The subtraction of 14 from 24, 10 from 14, 4 from 10 and so on would be done in the head or on the fingers. A calculator who knew $2\ 4s$ would of course omit the last line.

(2)

$$24 \times 14 = (19 + 5)(19 - 5)$$
$$= 19^2 - 5^2 = 361 - 25 = 336$$

The fact that $(19 + 5)(19 - 5)$ was equivalent to $19^2 - 5^2$ may have been discovered through work on area. 19 is the

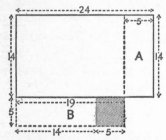

arithmetic mean of 24 and 14, i.e. the number half-way between them, and if as shown, instead of the rectangle 24 by 14 we take the dotted square 19 by 19, we have removed a strip 14 by 5 (A) and replaced it by a strip 19 by 5 (B). Hence the square is 5 by 5 too large and the original 24 by 14 rectangle is equal in area to the 19 by 19 square with a 5 by 5 square removed.

When we try to multiply an odd and an even number, say 24×15, by this method we have an arithmetic mean which is not a whole number—in this case $19\frac{1}{2}$. This difficulty can be overcome as follows

$$24 \times 15 = 23 \times 15 + 15$$
$$= (19 + 4)(19 - 4) + 15$$
$$= 19^2 - 4^2 + 15$$
$$= 361 - 16 + 15 = 360.$$

Nichomachus of Alexandria who wrote a work in two volumes on arithmetic about the end of the first century A.D., describes these methods of using the difference of two squares in multiplication. He also gives a method for extending the table of squares; thus for 122^2 the method he suggests would proceed as follows:

$$122^2 - 22^2 = (122 - 22)(122 + 22)$$
$$= 100 \times 144$$
$$\therefore 122^2 = 100 \times 144 + 22^2.$$

Hence given the ability to multiply 144 by 100, a matter of moving the counters two places along on the abacus, the value of 122^2 could be obtained by adding on, again on the abacus, the value of 22^2 obtained from the table.

It is probable that some calculators developed methods of multiplication with the abacus which somewhat resembled the methods we use to-day. This would only be possible for those who developed considerable familiarity with number relationships or ability with tables, and who had a real sense of the principle of place value implicit in the use of the abacus. Given these two accomplishments the multiplication of 24×14 may have proceeded as follows:

$$20 \times 10 = 200$$
$$4 \times 10 = 40 \text{ giving } 240$$
$$20 \times 4 = 80 \quad , \quad 320$$
$$4 \times 4 = 16 \quad , \quad 336$$

the abacus showing successively the values 200, 240, 320 and 336. The more expert may even have reduced the steps to

$$20 \times 14 = 280$$
$$4 \times 14 = 56 \text{ giving } 336,$$

particularly when comprehensive tables were available. Such methods show a clearer appreciation of the concept of multiplication than those which used repeated addition or duplation. We know that some Greek, Roman and Chinese calculators reached this level. These methods seem obvious when the problem is set out in our numerals. If, however, we consider it when written as

$$\langle\langle \Upsilon\Upsilon\Upsilon\Upsilon \text{ times} \langle \Upsilon\Upsilon\Upsilon\Upsilon \text{ or } XXIV \text{ times} XIV$$

we may be less surprised that such methods have not always been used.

We return now to consider the development of division from the method of repeated subtraction already described. A form of division used by the Egyptians was based on doubling and halving; the work was arranged somewhat as shown in the following division of 21 by 8 though, of course, the Egyptians did not use modern numerals.

1	8
2	16
$\frac{1}{2}$	4
$\frac{1}{4}$	2
$\frac{1}{8}$	1

As $21 = 16 + 4 + 1$ it follows that $2 + \frac{1}{2} + \frac{1}{8}$ 8s $= 21$ or that 8 goes into 21 $2 + \frac{1}{2} + \frac{1}{8}$ times.

As with the two other methods already described—the repeated subtraction and the trial multiplication—this method is concerned with finding how many times one number *goes into* another. This is not, however, the only type of question that we answer by division; there are also problems of *sharing*. In sharing we are dividing into a given number of parts; in the 'goes into' problems we are dividing into parts of a given size. As an example of sharing we may consider the division of a flock of 864 sheep into 6 equal groups. The reader may find it interesting to work out how this problem could be solved using the abacus. The problem is not difficult if looked on as the arranging of counters in 6 equal groups.

None of the methods mentioned—repeated subtraction, trial multiplication, halving and doubling, arranging in equal groups—shows any real appreciation of division. Division as carried out to-day is an operation in its own right which makes use of number relationships and which can be used to solve both 'goes into' and 'sharing' problems. But the concept of a quotient seems to have proved particularly difficult to the human mind. Of the methods of calculation in use in Europe by the tenth century it is in division that the difference from modern methods is most marked. Gerbert, who became Pope Sylvester II in A.D. 999, gave ten cases of division with the abacus, beginning with the division of units by units by continued subtraction. His cases include division by the use of complementary differences—a method which shows the beginnings of the idea of a quotient. In this the next higher multiple of 10 was used as divisor and at each stage compensation was made by replacing the appropriate multiple of the difference. In the following example of $1726 \div 18$ we use 20 as divisor and replace appropriate multiples of 2 (i.e., $20 - 18$).

Division of 1726 by 18

$$
\begin{array}{rr}
 & 1726 \\
80 \times 20 = & 1600 \\
\hline
\text{leaving} & 126 \\
\text{replacing } 80 \times 2 = & 160 \\
\hline
\text{we have} & 286 \\
10 \times 20 = & 200 \\
\hline
\text{leaving} & 86 \\
\text{replacing } 10 \times 2 = & 20 \\
\hline
\text{we have} & 106 \\
5 \times 20 = & 100 \\
\hline
\text{leaving} & 6 \\
\text{replacing } 5 \times 2 = & 10 \\
\text{we have} & 16. \\
\end{array}
$$

Hence final quotient $= 80 + 10 + 5 = 95$ and remainder is 16.

The above example is, of course, only a reproduction on paper of the method used. In practice the numbers shown in the right-hand column would be expressed in turn on the abacus—we would first have 1726, then 1600 removed leaving 126, then 160 placed under it and added on and so on; the successive quotients were recorded on a different part of the abacus, usually the bottom. By Gerbert the numbers would usually be expressed by placing in each column a single counter with the appropriate numeral written on it; these counters, the apices, will be discussed in the next chapter.

Commenting on Gerbert's rules of division, Florian Cajori says that they appear to have been framed to avoid subtractions as much as possible, to restrict the use of multiplication tables to the multiplication of numbers of single digits only, and to allow the operation to proceed in a purely mechanical way. In the above example, $286 \div 20$ for instance results first in 10×20 and not 14×20, and all the subtractions are of the $106 - 100$ variety.

The Persistence of the Abacus

Some of the methods described above show how complex peoples of earlier times found calculations which we can do quite quickly. It is surprising to realize that calculation was tied to the abacus until comparatively recent times. As already mentioned this was partly due to the scarcity of writing materials and even more to the unsuitability of the number symbols for written calculation. In earlier times written symbols were used to record partial and final answers obtained on the abacus, but the idea of using symbols to carry out calculations is a fairly recent development.

A few able Alexandrian mathematicians did succeed in using written methods but it is not difficult to see why the practice did not become widespread. Their single code symbols may have facilitated the use of number relationships but as they did not use the principle of place value they had twenty-seven symbols and hence many more relationships between symbols than we have. In view of the Greeks' great achievements in other branches of mathematics it may seem surprising that they did not devise a system of numerals more suitable for use in calculation. It should be remembered, however, that many Greek mathematicians were inclined to despise calculation (logistica) and to regard it as unworthy of their attention. They were much more interested in the theory of numbers (arithmetica) and had considerable knowledge of the properties of numbers; Nichomachus, for example, knew that the cube of any number could be expressed as the sum of that number of consecutive odd numbers ($2^3 = 3 + 5$, $3^3 = 7 + 9 + 11$, $4^3 = 13 + 15 + 17 + 19$ and so on). The Greeks had many strange beliefs about numbers, in fact their superstitions about numbers in many ways resembled those of the Chinese; most numbers up to fifty, for example, were identified with some human quality. The extent of their number worship can be gauged from the following extract from the Pythagorean's prayer to the number four, 'Bless us, divine number, thou who generatest gods and men! O holy, holy tetraktys thou that containest the root and the source of the eternally flowing creation!'

The Romans' widespread empire and methods of government made reckoning and accounts of considerable importance, but nevertheless they did not develop written methods of calculation. Roman numerals were used in Europe for nearly 2,000 years but with them there was little possibility of developing written methods. In the Middle Ages the abacus was sometimes drawn on paper or parchment or later on the slate. This development may be regarded as a slight move towards written calculations, but the methods used were fundamentally the same as those used with actual counters on the abacus and, of course, in many cases the board and counters were still used. Even when written methods of calculation were adopted in Europe the influence of abacus methods still remained and duplation and mediation were frequently included in 'the rules of arithmetic'.

The influence of the use of the abacus is seen to-day in our word 'calculate' (to pebble) and also in such words as 'counter'. The table or board on which a merchant of the Middle Ages reckoned his customer's account was called a 'counting table' or 'counter', and we still speak of 'buying over the counter', though shopkeepers have for long reckoned with pencils and paper and have no lines scored on their tables. Our word 'exchequer' has a similar derivation. At one time the Court of Exchequer was a court of law at which the financial business of the crown was also carried on. The table at which the judges and officers sat was covered with black cloth divided into squares or chequers by white lines. This 'chessboard' (from medieval Latin 'scaccarium') was used as an abacus in making up Exchequer accounts.

CHAPTER IV

THE MODERN NUMBER SYSTEM

'The interesting point to notice is the admirable illustration which this numeral system affords of the enormous importance of a good notation. By relieving the brain of all unnecessary work, a good notation sets it free to concentrate on more advanced problems, and in effect increases the mental power of the race.'

A. N. WHITEHEAD
in *An Introduction to Mathematics*

IT is difficult for us to-day to dissociate any idea of number from the number symbols with which we are so familiar. It should be clear, however, from the preceding chapters that man developed considerable facility with number before he used any written number symbols at all, and that our present system is by no means the only system of written numerals which has been used. Most peoples evolved their own separate systems when they began to record numbers, and modern numerals have only been in common use for about four centuries. Even to-day they are unknown in many parts of the world, and other numerals such as the Chinese and Arabic are used by millions of people.

The Origin of the Number Symbols we use To-day

There has been considerable controversy about the origin of our numerals. The most widely accepted theory is that they are of Hindu origin, were brought to Spain by the Moors in the eighth or ninth century A.D. when the Moslem empire extended to Spain in the west and the Indus in the east, and were later transmitted to Christian Europe. For this reason they are frequently called the 'Hindu-Arabic' numerals, though as their present form developed in Europe some prefer to refer to them as the 'European numerals'; others use the term 'modern numerals', and in the thirteenth or fourteenth century the misleading title 'Arabic numerals' became common and is still sometimes used to-day.

Examples of early Indian numerals were given in Chapter II and the reader may have noticed similarities between some of those and some of the numerals which we use to-day. We do not know how early the Arabs began to use Indian numerals; they were probably introduced in the eighth century and it would seem that for most purposes they had replaced the use of the letters of the Arabic alphabet by the ninth century. The present-day Arabic numerals shown here are the result of subsequent modifications in those originally adopted. It is, of course, to these that the

term 'Arabic numerals' can be properly applied.

There were several differences between the numerals adopted by the eastern Arabs and those transmitted to Europe. The symbols used by the Spanish Arabs were called the *gobar* or dust numerals from their connexion with the Hindu dust abacus and as distinguished from the Arabic alphabetic numerals. The oldest known example of the numerals used in Europe is as shown. They are from the

Codex Vigilanus written in Spain in A.D. 976. An important influence in the introduction of the Hindu numerals into Europe was a book written by the great Arab mathematician al-Khowarazmi in about A.D. 825. It is considered probable that the numerals used by al-Khowarazmi and those adopted by the eastern Arabs were of different forms. There were local differences in both letters and numerals used in India, and these two forms may have come from different sources or by different routes. In all such considerations we have to remember, too, the changes which inevitably occur when symbols are copied by hand; different writers stress different aspects of a symbol and some add ornamental flourishes. Al-Khowarazmi's book was later translated into

Latin with the title *Liber Algorismi de Numero Indorum* (The Book of al-Khowarazmi on Hindu number), 'Algorismus' being the medieval Latin rendering of the name 'al-Khowarazmi'. The translation is usually attributed to Adelard of Bath, a twelfth-century English monk. The fact that this book was translated from the Arabic may have been partly responsible for the later use of the term 'Arabic numerals' in referring to our numerals.

It would not be useful here to refer in detail to the variation in the shapes of the Hindu-Arabic numerals used in European manuscripts before the introduction of printing, but it may be of interest to refer to some of the main trends. Most of the symbols denoting one, two, three, six, eight and nine bear considerable resemblance to our 1, 2, 3, 6, 8 and 9; but two was sometimes denoted by $\mathcal{T}$ (when this symbol is inverted it resembles 2), various other symbols were also used to denote three, and there was some variation in the slope of the top of the symbol for 6. There have been greater changes in the symbols for four, five and seven. In earlier manuscripts a common form for four was $\mathcal{R}$; this was sometimes written $\mathcal{9}$ and from this the present form developed. Five was usually written $\mathcal{y}$; in some cases this was written $\mathcal{Y}$—hence probably the present 5. Seven was usually denoted by two intersecting strokes frequently written Λ, though sometimes $\mathcal{>}$ and other positions. The introduction of printing in the fifteenth century led to greater uniformity in forms of the numerals, and there has been little change in the last four centuries. Minor differences do exist (seven is denoted $\mathcal{7}$ in some countries) but international communication in science, commerce and other affairs is greatly facilitated by the widespread use of a comparatively uniform set of number symbols.

The Importance of the Hindu System

The form of the symbols is not, however, the most important feature of our system of numerals. Any other set of

symbols would serve equally well once we became familiar
with them, provided they were easy to write and easily
distinguished from one another. The widespread adoption
of the Indian system was not due to the form of the symbols
used. Indeed, the Indian symbols were probably known
to Europeans for several centuries before any particular
attention was paid to them. Merchants would know them as
the numeral signs on goods from India, but the early system
described on page 43, with symbols for units and multiples
of ten, and symbols for a hundred and a thousand used as
labels rather as in the Chinese system, had no particular
advantage over other code systems in use.

It was when the Indian system was developed so as to
combine three important features that it became noteworthy. These features were the use of

(a) single code symbols,

(b) the principle of place value,

(c) a zero symbol.

These remain the most important features of our number
system to-day and merit further consideration here.

The earlier Indian system, of course, had code symbols,
and as we saw in Chapter II single code symbols had been
used in other systems. Whether code symbols evolved
gradually or were adopted deliberately, they were preferred
by the peoples who used them because of their greater convenience in recording numbers. This is still an important
consideration, but even more important is the way in which
single symbols facilitate the use of number relationships in
written calculation. Conciseness is an important quality in
a symbolism, and if the sum of three and four is obtained
not by counting, but is known because the relationship
between three, four and seven is firmly established in the
mind, it is appropriate that the numbers should be represented by single symbols. We may say that

$$III + IIII = \begin{matrix} IIII \\ III \end{matrix} \text{ symbolizes an operation based on counting}$$

$$\text{while } 3 + 4 = 7 \quad \text{symbolizes a relationship between numbers.}$$

The conciseness of the Hindu numerals was an important factor in the development of written calculation.

Conciseness of symbolism alone, however, is not enough. Other systems with equally concise code symbols could not have been used with equal facility in written calculation, for they did not apply (b)—the principle of place value. With the Greek system and others which had a different set of symbols for units, ten and hundreds, calculation would have been much more complex; as has been pointed out, such systems obscure the parallel between $2 + 2$ and $20 + 20$, and with them, too, it would have been necessary to know separate sets of number relationships when multiplying by 20 and 200 instead of merely applying those used when multiplying by 2.

As we saw in Chapter II, however, given a real appreciation of the structure of a number system, it is not necessary or desirable either to use different symbols for different collective units or to denote each collective unit by a label symbol. The position of a symbol relative to its fellows is sufficient indication of the collective unit involved. This principle was applied of course in the Babylonian sexagesimal system and the Mayan vigesimal system, but these had not a concise symbolism and so would not have lent themselves to written calculation based on number relationships. In both there were tallying symbols repeated the appropriate number of times; with bases as large as 60 and 20 it would hardly have been possible to have single code symbols—the task of remembering the values of so many different symbols would have been enormous.

The Hindus in their system achieved the combined advantages of a concise symbolism and of the principle of place value. As a result they then needed only nine different symbols, and their written representation of numbers was brought closer to the representation of numbers on the abacus, thus increasing the possibility of performing symbolically in writing the operations of the abacus.

It is worth noting that the advantages of conciseness and of the principle of place value were also achieved by the use of apices on the abacus. Apices were counters each with one of nine number symbols drawn on it. The number seven, for example, was denoted on the abacus by one counter marked with a symbol for seven, instead of by seven separate counters or one counter to denote five and two further separate counters. To some extent the introduction of the apices may be regarded as a continuation of the trend which led to intermediate replacement; it was not, however, a step taken by all peoples who became proficient in the use of the abacus. Our first definite information about the use of the apices is from a treatise written by Gerbert towards the end of the tenth century, but it is possible that they were used considerably earlier. The number symbols on the apices are clearly of Hindu origin. Until the sixteenth century the name 'apices' was commonly used to refer to the Hindu-Arabic numerals.

Calculation with the apices was essentially based on number relationships; it was not possible to count out individual counters. The use of the apices led to a gain in conciseness, for any number could be denoted by placing not more than one counter in any one column of the abacus. As the column gave the symbol a place value, the same set of symbols could be used in each column and hence only one set of number relationships was involved as in modern written calculation. The disadvantage in the use of the apices was the time spent in finding the required counters to place on the abacus. In written calculation, of course, this disadvantage does not exist. But Gerbert and his contemporaries could not have made the step from the abacus to written calculation for they did not appreciate the significance of (c)—a zero symbol. On the abacus a zero symbol was not necessary; the number four hundred and seven, for example, was recorded by placing a counter marked four in the hundreds column and one marked seven in the units column. The fact that the tens column was left empty showed that there were no tens. But in writing, if the symbols 4 and 7 are written thus 4 7 it is not possible to be certain whether or not there is a space, or even two spaces, between them. A zero symbol placed between them contributes nothing to the total but it serves to keep the symbol 4 in the third place. This idea of representing emptiness or nothingness by a symbol has proved difficult for the human mind.

The use of a zero symbol was a great achievement by the Hindus. It has been described as 'practically one of the greatest moves ever made in science'. It enabled Hindu calculators to leave the columns of the abacus and to develop methods of written calculation. The symbol originally used by the Hindus was a dot which they called 'sunyabindu' (the dot marking a blank). They did not, it would seem, think of it as denoting a number but as indicating an empty space. The idea of regarding nothingness or emptiness as a number is at least as difficult as the idea of representing emptiness by a symbol. The idea of number is subtle and difficult to analyse whether we are considering zero or any of the other numbers. What makes the idea of the other numbers less difficult is the fact that we are familiar with their use—we do handle three books and five pencils whereas we would hardly go to the cupboard for zero books or zero pencils. A vagueness in our conception of zero is perhaps indicated by the variety of names used to refer to the zero symbol; we have naught, nothing, nil, O (the name of the letter) as well as zero and cipher. The last two, it may be noted, both derive from the Hindu 'sunya'. In Arabic 'sunya' became 'as-sifr' or 'sifr' which led to the Latin 'zephirum' in Italy in the thirteenth century, and hence eventually to the Italian 'zero' which appeared in manuscript in the middle of the fourteenth century. The English 'cipher', the French 'chiffre' and others clearly derive from 'sifr'; in many languages the word has come to mean the numeral figures in general.

The wider conception of zero as a number probably developed through the use of the zero symbol with the symbols for the other numbers. This conception, of course, is essential in modern calculation where we deal with the values of individual symbols, and consequently the relationships used may involve zero as well as other numbers.

Relationships involving zero do seem liable to cause particular difficulty and yet the ideas involved seem simple enough. There is nothing particularly difficult about such ideas as

(i) a thing is unchanged when nothing is added to it;

(ii) if a thing is taken no times nothing is obtained;

(iii) when nothing is shared nobody gets anything.

Perhaps the difficulty is due more to the idea of treating nothing as a number and representing it by a symbol, than to the special nature of the relationships.

The Adoption of the Hindu System

We cannot be definite about the date of the introduction of the principle of place value and the zero symbol into the Hindu system. It is doubtful if the complete system was in common use before the eighth century A.D., though it is thought to have originated in the sixth century. The origin of the system will probably always remain a mystery; possibly the introduction of place value and the zero symbol was more a matter of gradual development than of sudden invention. It has been suggested that the Hindu method of naming the powers of ten may have aided this development. Their reading of the number 254,163 would have been

2 laskas, 5 ayutas, 4 sahasra, 1 sata, 6 dasan, 3.

This independent naming of each collective unit shows a much more consistent application of the decimal system than is found in other languages. It would help to bring out the idea of place value, and would also make it more necessary to have a word to denote the absence of a unit, particularly as the order of the names used for the collective units varied in different districts. The use of the abacus would also encourage the idea of place value, and it is possible that Hindu astronomers met the application of the principle in the Babylonian sexagesimal fractions which they used.

The introduction of place value and the zero symbol seems a simple way of making possible the written expression of the procedure of the abacus, and to us the advantages of such a device are clear enough. By performing an operation symbolically the work is simplified, and it becomes possible to extend the operation to more complex forms. But to peoples unaccustomed to written calculation and not possessing cheap paper and pencils the advantages were much less apparent, and the new system was by no means immediately and enthusiastically adopted in other countries. It was his recognition of the importance of the new system that led al-Khowarazmi to write his book, and the influence of this book is indicated by the use in Europe of the name 'algorism' to refer to written calculation using Hindu-Arabic numerals. In Europe the introduction of the new system met with considerable resistance and there was antagonism between the algorists using 'the art of al-Khowarazmi' and the abacists who continued to use the methods of the counting board.

It is important to distinguish between the inconspicuous entrance into Europe of the Hindu number symbols, and the introduction later of the system with the principle of place value and the zero symbol. It has been suggested that the symbols may have been known in Alexandria in the fifth century A.D. or even earlier, and that they were carried from there along the shores of the Mediterranean by traders. Gerbert's treatise on the apices helped to make Hindu symbols known to scholars. He does not, however, appear to have known of their use with place value and a zero symbol; he used them only for calculation, and not in his written works. The abacists following Gerbert continued to use the counting board and the Roman numerals. It was not until the thirteenth century that the Hindu-Arabic system was at all widely used in Christian Europe. It was known earlier to some merchants and scholars, and some treatises had been written on the algorism, but these had little effect in spreading the new system. Leonardo of Pisa (sometimes called Leonardo Fibonacci) played a considerable part in making the advantages of the Hindu-Arabic system more widely known. Leonardo was born in 1175 when Pisa was one of the great commercial centres in Italy and while he was a boy his father, a merchant, was sent to control the customs house at Bugia in North Africa. Leonardo was educated there and as a young man he travelled considerably and knew the methods of numeration used by the merchants of different countries. He considered the Hindu-Arabic system superior to all others and in 1202 published in Pisa his book *Liber Abaci* in which he explained the system and pointed out its advantages over the Roman system; he also explained written methods of calculation, in order, he said, that 'the Latin race might no longer be deficient in that knowledge'.

Two other works which did much to make the use of the Hindu-Arabic numerals more widely known were the *Algorismus* written by Sacrobosco (John of Halifax) and *Carmen de Algorismo* a short arithmetic in Latin verse by Alexander de Villa Dei; both were written about the middle of the thirteenth century.

The algorism naturally appealed most to those who had to carry out intricate calculations. By the middle of the thirteenth century it was much used by men of science, particularly astronomers; indeed, without it, the revival in astronomy of that time would have been impossible. Its advantages in commerce also became more and more widely recognized in the thirteenth and fourteenth centuries, particularly in Italy, then the greatest trading country in Europe. The use of the Hindu-Arabic numerals aroused much opposition. In 1299, for example, merchants in Florence were forbidden to use them and were ordered either to use Roman numerals or to write the number words; in some places they were banned from official documents. Such opposition was partly due to conservatism, but partly also due to the possibilities of misunderstanding and fraudulent alteration when the new numerals were used. The Roman numerals were of course much better known, and the existing methods of writing them made alterations almost impossible; for example, seven was written 'vij' to prevent the addition of further strokes. In the days before printing, knowledge spread slowly, but gradually through their use by merchants and scholars, and on almanacs and calendars, the new symbols and the algoristic arithmetic became widely known and used in Europe. Hindu-Arabic numerals were rarely used in England, France and Germany until the middle of the fifteenth century, though they are found in some manuscripts of the thirteenth century. Even in the first half of the sixteenth century most English merchants continued to use Roman numerals in keeping their accounts. Two works which influenced the adoption of the new symbols in England were *De Arte Supputandi* by Cuthbert Tonstall, published in Latin in 1522, and *The Grounde of Artes* by Robert Recorde, published in English in 1540. It is interesting to note that Recorde describes methods of calculation with counters as well as with symbols. The adoption of the new numerals did not always lead at once to the adoption of written methods of calculation. The Hindu-Arabic numerals were in general use in Europe by the sixteenth century but there was some use of the lined abacus for another century; its reduced status can, however, be gauged from the fact that the term 'counter caster' appears to have been used to express contempt for anyone's poor ability in calculation.

Early Methods of Written Calculation

The methods of written calculation developed by Hindu, Arab and European calculators differed in several ways from those used to-day. Hindu and Arab calculators frequently worked from left to right when adding or subtracting, figures being altered when 'carrying' or 'borrowing' made this necessary. In some Arab works the answer was written above the numbers to be added or subtracted; in early European addition the sum of each column was sometimes written down and then these partial sums added. These differences in arrangement are comparatively unimportant, but there have been, and still are, more important differences in procedure in subtraction when a larger digit appears under a smaller one. In *The Crafte of Nombrynge* (*c.* 1300) one of the first works on the algorism written in English—possibly a translation and amplification of one of

the glosses on de Villa Dei's work—there is a description of
the subtraction of 1,134 from 2,122 which begins 'take 4 out
of 2. it wyl not be, þerfore borro one of þe next
figure . . . and ·sett þat ouer þe hed of þe fyrst
2. & rekene it for ten.' This leaves 1 in the
second place. Then 4 is taken out of ten leaving 6; the 2
above the 4 is 'cast' to the 6 'and þat wylle be 8'. The expression 'cast' is obviously a relic from the use of the abacus.
This method of subtracting from a borrowed ten and then
adding the result to the original figure was also described
by Bhaskara, a Hindu mathematician of the twelfth century
and by various European writers of the fifteenth and sixteenth centuries; it should be noted that in this method only
differences from ten are used. In another method which has
also been used for many centuries, in the example 53—27,
the fifty-three would be regarded as forty-thirteen, as it
were, and the 7 subtracted from the 13 and the 20 from the
40. The principle of this method is the same as that of the
method of subtraction on the abacus described on page 63;
compared with the first method described it avoids the final
addition but does not involve only differences from ten.
Rabbi ben Ezra (c. 1140), in a description of this method,
advises beginning at the left and looking ahead to take care
of borrowing. In another method which was known early in
Europe the subtraction of 27 from 53 would again begin
with 7 from 13, but the 1 would·be repaid by adding to the
lower line, making the final step the subtraction of 3 from
5. The relevance of this procedure is less obvious than that
of the other two methods. The method is, however, thought
by some to lead to speedier working and finds considerable
favour to-day. There are, of course, other methods which
have been used and are still used, but these three illustrate
the main differences.

In considering Hindu methods of written calculation it is
important to remember the influence of their writing-
materials and of their earlier use of the dust abacus. They
wrote either with a cane pen using thin, white paint on a
þlackboard, or with a small stick on a white tablet strewn

with red flour. In either case there was not room to write many symbols at a time but it was easy to erase a symbol and write another in its place. Because of this, the need in working from left to right, to alter some symbols, would not appear to be a particular disadvantage. The effect of the limited space is seen in the following multiplication of 263 by 24; the appearance of the board after each step is shown. (a)–(d) show the multiplication of 263 by 2 (the left-hand

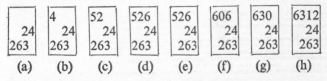

(a)   (b)   (c)   (d)   (e)   (f)   (g)   (h)

digit of the multiplier), the product being written above; (e) shows the board after the figures 2, 6 and 3 were erased and re-written one place to the right ready for multiplication by 4. The Hindus did not write down the result of this multiplication and then add it to the first result as we do using pencil and paper. The result of the multiplication of each digit was added on as the work proceeded; thus in (f) the 52 has been changed to 60 as a result of adding on 4×2 (the first step in the multiplication by 4).

In this method the work proceeded in a systematic manner; the units digit of the number to be multiplied was always placed under the digit to be used as multiplier, and the result of each multiplication was added to the digit above the one multiplied. The method had, however, the disadvantage that it was not possible to check earlier steps in the working.

When Arab calculators adopted this method the successive steps in their working were somewhat as shown below. As the Arabs worked on paper they could not easily erase digits; instead, when a digit was to be altered they crossed it out and wrote the new one immediately above or below it. This resulted in the digits of a number not always being kept in a row, for example, the 2 of the answer 6,312 is two rows below the other digits.

					6	63	631
		5	5	5	50	500	500
	4	42	426	426	426	426	4262
24	24	24	24	24	24	24	24
263	263	263	263	2633	2633	2633	2633
				26	26	26	26
(a)	(b)	(c)	(d)	(e)	(f)	(g)	(h)

It does not appear to have occurred to the Arabs that their less restricted space made a more convenient arrangement possible.

In another method used by the Hindus, though possibly of Arabic origin, the tablet was divided into squares with diagonals drawn as shown. The number to be multiplied

was written along the top and the multiplier down the side, the highest power in each being placed nearest to the top left corner. In each square, the product of the digits opposite that square was written; for example, the middle square of the bottom row has the digit 4 on its left and 6 above it, and as their product is 24, the digit 2 is written in the top left half of the square, and 4 in the bottom right half. The final result was obtained by adding diagonally. This is a neat method which proceeds automatically and does not take up much space. A similar arrangement, sometimes with the diagonals sloping the other way was also used by Italian and Chinese calculators.

The main idea of this 'grating method' was also used in Napier's rods which were described in the *Rabdologia* published in 1617. At that time the multiplication of large numbers gave difficulty to all but professional calculators, and Napier's aim was 'to do away with the difficulty and tediousness of calculations, the irksomeness of which is wont to deter very many from the study of mathematics'. Each rod was divided into nine small squares and had one of the digits 1–9 written in the top square. The remaining eight squares

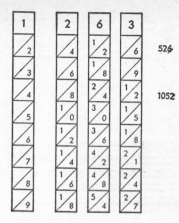

were divided diagonally and contained respectively the results of multiplying the number in the top square by 2, 3, 4, 5, 6, 7, 8, 9. The rods for 1, 2, 6 and 3 are shown.

Having placed them thus it is easy to read off the products 2 × 263 and 4 × 263 and to obtain the product of 24 and 263 as shown. A device similar to the rods had long been in use in India and Persia. Napier's rods attracted considerable attention in Europe and also in China and Japan.

$$\begin{array}{r} 263 \\ \hline 1052/4 \\ 526/2 \\ \hline 6312 \end{array}$$

To the Hindus, multiplication by any method was a difficult process, and as their practice of erasing digits as a calculation proceeded made it impossible to check over the steps of their working, it was important to have some method of checking the final result. Among the methods used for this purpose was the 'casting out of the nines'. This can be illustrated by referring again to their multiplication of 263 by 24. In this the final appearance of the tablet was as shown. In the casting out of the nines the sum of the digits of each number was obtained and the excess of

each sum over nine or a multiple of nine noted. Thus the digits 6, 3, 1 and 2 add up to 12 which is 3 in excess of 9; as many readers will realize this means that the number 6,312 is also 3 in excess of an exact multiple of 9. Similarly 24 and 263 are respectively 6 and 2 in excess of exact multiples of 9. The product of 24 and 263 will thus contain a number of complete 9s and 6×2, i.e. 12, over; the 12 will give one more complete 9 and a final excess of 3. As the answer 6312 and the product thus both have an excess of 3 the answer is considered to be checked. Although many who used it appear not to have been aware of the fact, it is not difficult to see that it is not a complete check—an error of 9, for example, would go undetected. Casting out the 9s was also used by the Arabs and by other peoples; it came into general use in the eleventh century and is found in many of the early arithmetics printed in Europe. It was used to check calculation on the abacus as well as written calculation; on the abacus the excess noted was the number of counters left after groups of 9 had been cast out.

Italian calculators, like the Hindus, knew many methods of multiplication, indeed they seem to have had a passion

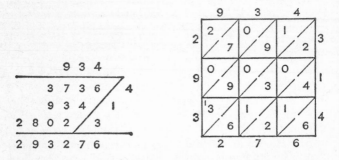

for inventing new forms. It would not be useful here to refer to more than a few of these methods. The first printed arithmetic was printed in Treviso in Italy in 1478. The above examples illustrate two of the ways in which the multiplication of 934 by 314 was set out in it; the second of the methods is the grating method already described. In his *Summa de Arithmetica*, published in 1494, Lucas Pacioli gave 8 different methods of multiplication, but the 'chess-board method' which he describes first was then generally preferred. This method may be illustrated by the following example: The name 'chessboard' is clearly due to the squares which were drawn and which served to keep the digits in the correct columns; in the course of time, however, they

were dispensed with. This method, now in common use, has been known by many different names and there has been considerable variety in the arrangement of the working. In some works the multiplier was placed above the number to be multiplied; in the Treviso arithmetic it was placed to the right. There have also been differences in the placing of the digits of the multiplier—in the above example some writers would have placed the 2 of the 24 under the 2 of the 263.

Other methods described by Pacioli included 'the castle method', cross multiplication, the grating method, multiplication by factors (e.g., $234 \times 48 = 234 \times 6 \times 8$) and multiplication by parts (e.g., $163 \times 17 = 163 \times 10 + 163 \times 7$ or $163 \times 20 - 163 \times 3$). In the castle method, multiplication began with the left-hand digit of the multiplier, and the appropriate number of zeros were filled in in the partial products. In cross-multiplication the digits were written as shown and the products of those at the ends of each line drawn from the top row to the bottom row obtained; these products were then added. It is possible that this method suggested the X sign for multiplication.

The Hindus and Arabs rarely used multiplication tables, but in Italy the use of tables at least as far as 5×5 became common. We have already seen how it is possible from this to obtain any product up to 10×10 by using the fingers. A written method similar to the finger method was given by several sixteenth-century writers; it was frequently referred to as the 'sluggard's rule'. To obtain 7×9 the digits 7 and 9 were written as shown and opposite them their differences from 10, viz.

3 and 1. The tens digit of the product was then obtained by subtracting either the 3 from the 9 or the 1 from the 7 (cross-subtraction so to speak). The units digit was obtained by multiplying the 1 and the 3.

Method of Division

In view of the difficulty which multiplication presented to early calculators, it is not surprising that for a long time division was looked on as an operation to be performed only by skilled mathematicians. There are two important methods of division to be noted—the galley or scratch method, and the method of long division which is used to-day. Other methods used included short division and division by factors. A form of short division was given in the Treviso arithmetic; it was used for any divisor included in the multiplication tables. Division by factors, of course, followed from this; it was given by Italian writers and was common in the late Middle Ages.

Our modern method of long division is a comparatively recent invention. It was known in Italy in the fourteenth century but the method then in common use in that country was the 'galley method'. This method can be explained by showing the successive steps in the division of 8,217 by 34.

(a)   (b)   (c)   (d)   (e)   (f)

(g)   (h)   (i)

(a) shows the digits written down ready for the first part of the division. In (b) 2 has been written in the quotient and 2×3 subtracted from 8 which is scratched out and the remainder 2 written above it; as the 3 in the divisor has been used in this position it too is scratched out. Similarly in (c) since 2×4 subtracted from 22 leaves 14 the twos have been scratched out and 1 and 4 written in the places above them; the 4 of the divisor has also been scratched out. In (d) the divisor 34 has been written one place to the right ready for the second part of the division; this proceeds in the same way as is shown in (e) and (f). In (g) the digits 3 and 4 have been written another place to the right, ready for the third and last part which is shown in (h) and (i). The final appearance of the working was as shown in (i). This method, as one might guess from its resemblance to the method of multiplication given on page 92, was developed from a Hindu method in which the figures were erased after use. It was used by Arab calculators from the time of al-Khowarazmi; in Europe it was for long used, with variations in some details, almost to the exclusion of other methods, not only by commercial calculators, but also by some mathematicians and scientists—it is given in the works of Tonstall, Recorde, Stevin, Napier and others. The method, though perhaps difficult to us at first sight, does, in fact, proceed smoothly, and is more compact and involves fewer figures than our present method. The name 'galley' comes from the resemblance of the outline of the completed working to a boat or galley. Pacioli considered it the swiftest method just as the galley was the swiftest ship. In an example by a Venetian monk of the sixteenth century, the division of 965,347,655,446 by 6,543, the work is ornamented to make it resemble a galley; it is said that some Venetian teachers required such illustrations from their pupils. The galley method was in use in Italy until about 1600, and in other countries until much later. In England, where it was known as the *scratch method*, it was not superseded until the beginning of the eighteenth century. It is probable that the Pilgrim Fathers took the scratch method with them to

America; in recent times it was still in use in Morocco and there considered superior to our method.

It is not possible to be definite about the time and place of origin of our modern method of long division. It has been suggested that it may have developed from a column method found in various Arab and Persian works. Using this method the same division, i.e. of 8,217 by 34, would have appeared somewhat as shown in (p). At each stage each

```
        2   4   1   (quotient)

    8   2   1   7
    6
    ──────────────
    2   2   1   7
        8
    ──────────────
    1   4   1   7
    1   2
    ──────────────
        2   1   7
        1   6
    ──────────────
            5   7
            3
    ──────────────
            2   7
                4
    ──────────────
            2   3   (remainder)

            8̶   4̶       (divisor)
    8̶   4̶
```

```
34)8217(241        34)8217(241
    6                  68
   ──                 ──
   22                 14
    8                141
  ───                136
  141                ───
   12                  5
   ──                 57
   21                 34
   16                 ──
  ───                 23
   57
    3
   ──
   27
    4
   ──
   23
```

(p)   (q)   (r)

digit in the divisor was used separately; thus in the first stage, after 2 had been entered in the quotient, first 6 and then 8 were subtracted, and each time the complete remainder was written down. There are clear similarities between this method and the present one, though in some respects it resembles the galley method. A later Arab method (q), given by Maximus Planudes, a fourteenth-century monk, comes nearer to our method. The arrangement (r) which is effectively the same as the modern method was in use in the fifteenth century. It was given the name 'a danda' (by giving) because after each subtraction the next figure was brought down and 'given' to the remainder; as can be seen, the remainder was repeated before the giving. The 'a danda' method was given in Calandri's work of 1491 and Pacioli in 1494 gives it as his third method. In sixteenth-century works it was given more frequently, but often as a matter of interest rather than as a method to use; as already mentioned, it was not until the seventeenth century that it began to replace the galley method even in Italy. In this method the quotient has been placed in various positions; many writers placed it to the right, but by some it was placed below the number to be divided—an awkward arrangement. The present habit of placing it above has advantages which were not so apparent until the use of decimal fractions became common.

The Development of Decimal Fractions

Modern facility in calculation is not due to the algorism alone. Two more recent developments—the use of decimal fractions and of logarithms—also play an important part; these will be considered separately.

The use of decimal fractions extends the scope of the algorism to include calculations involving fractional parts, for decimal fractions can be represented on a system of place value and hence methods used with whole numbers can be used in calculations with 'parts'.

Before considering the origin of our decimal fractions it may be useful to refer more generally to methods used in dealing with 'parts'. The consideration of fractional parts arises, of course, in situations involving some aspect of division, and from the earliest civilizations onwards man has attempted to deal with 'parts' in his reckoning. Such considerations have always caused difficulty to the human mind and for centuries man's conception of fractions was very limited. Most early attempts to deal with parts involved either

> (a) the creation of smaller units—*sub-units* as distinct from collective units

or (b) the use of *unit fractions,* i.e. fractions such as a third, a fifth, a tenth, which in modern notation would be written with 1 as numerator.

We are using the sub-unit approach when, instead of writing $\frac{3}{4}'$, we write $9''$, for we are expressing the part of the foot in terms of the smaller unit—the inch. This is a natural device to use in any form of measurement and it is not surprising to find that it was used by most peoples long before they developed more abstract and general ideas of fractions. Such a device does, of course, achieve the advantages of a common denominator.

Unit fractions involve more general ideas of fractions than do sub-units, but in practical situations they too occur more readily to the mind than other types of fractions. It is comparatively easy to form a picture of a part which is contained in the whole an exact number of times and to see, for example, that the part which is contained five times is less than that which is contained only three or four times; it is easier to visualize $\frac{1}{2}'' + \frac{1}{4}'' + \frac{1}{16}''$ than the same length expressed as $\frac{13}{16}''$. The Egyptians at an early date used unit fractions and developed a notation for expressing them. A fraction symbol ◠ was used in conjunction with the hieroglyphics for whole numbers, thus ⍓, ⍤ and ⍦ denoted a fifth, a tenth and a thirteenth. With the Greeks two accents served the same purpose, thus $''\varDelta$ represented $\frac{1}{4}$. The Egyptians built up tables to enable them to express other fractional values in terms of unit fractions. The result of dividing 2 into 43 equal parts was, for example, expressed in the

Ahmes Papyrus as the sum of $\frac{1}{42}$, $\frac{1}{86}$, $\frac{1}{129}$, $\frac{1}{301}$ (written of course in Egyptian symbols), though it is not clear why this particular set of unit fractions was preferred to other possibilities. In the Middle Ages unit fractions were known as 'simple fractions', to distinguish them from 'composite fractions', and some mathematicians still preferred to use them; Buteo for example in the sixteenth century gave the square of $1162\frac{1}{8}$ as $1350534\frac{1}{2}\frac{1}{64}$. Next to unit fractions, fractions such as $\frac{2}{3}$, $\frac{3}{4}$, $\frac{4}{5}$ are probably the simplest; these are equivalent to a whole with a unit fraction removed, and some peoples appear to have used these fractions more readily than other composite fractions. Such fractions remind one of the custom in some districts of describing a vessel roughly two-thirds full as 'two parts full', and one three-quarters full as 'three parts full'.

The ideas of more general composite fractions and of abstract fractions as numbers in their own rights, developed only slowly from the earlier limited and concrete ideas. The attempt to comprehend the composite fraction $\frac{3}{8}$ and to see it in relation to $\frac{5}{8}$ and $\frac{2}{8}$ does involve difficult ratio concepts —the comparison of relationships between numbers. In the Middle Ages most scientific writers favoured sexagesimal fractions, i.e. they expressed parts in $\frac{1}{60}$ths, $\frac{1}{3600}$ths, etc. These fractions had been developed by the Alexandrian astronomers when unit fractions began to prove inadequate for their work; they were used by the Arabs and passed from them to the algorists. The abacists on the other hand used the Roman duodecimal fractions. As an example of the use of sexagesimal fractions, we may note that in a tournament Leonardo of Pisa succeeded in approximating to one root of the equation $x^3 + 2x^2 + 10x = 20$ and gave the value of x as $1° \ 22' \ 7'' \ 4''' \ 33^{IV} \ 4^V \ 40^{VI}$ i.e. $1 + \frac{22}{60} + \frac{7}{60^2} + \ldots$; this when expressed in modern decimal fractions is correct to nine places. Leonardo also frequently used unit fractions and in the *Liber Abacus* he explains how to resolve a fraction into unit fractions.

With sexagesimal fractions, multiplication and division were complicated processes for which the aid of tables was almost essential. To us it seems strange to find 3° 23′ 54″ divided by 2° 34′ 24″ to give 1° 19′ 14″. To medieval scientists

it meant $$\frac{3 + \frac{23}{60} + \frac{54}{3600}}{2 + \frac{34}{60} + \frac{24}{3600}} = 1 + \frac{19}{60} + \frac{14}{3600}.$$

Various notations were used to express sexagesimal fractions. Most of them were more cumbersome than that used above but in all it was the power of 60 rather than the actual denominator which was given.

Sexagesimal and duodecimal fractions may both, of course, be regarded as a development of the sub-unit approach, and in that respect they resemble our decimal fractions in which parts are expressed in $\frac{1}{10}$ths, $\frac{1}{100}$ths, etc. Neither the sexagesimal nor the duodecimal fractions, however, could have been expressed by extending the system of place values; this is only possible when the same base is used for both whole numbers and fractional parts. The Babylonians achieved this, for as well as expressing whole numbers on a system with a base 60 they also developed the use of sexagesimal fractions, i.e. as well as recording 1s, 60s, 3,600s, etc. they also recorded $\frac{1}{60}$ths, $\frac{1}{3600}$ths, etc. They applied the principle of place value in denoting both the whole numbers and the parts, and thus anticipated the modern method of representing decimal fractions. There were ambiguities in the Babylonian system for they had no mark, corresponding to our decimal point, to separate symbols representing whole numbers from those representing fractions. Thus $\frac{1}{2}$ and $\frac{1}{3}$ were denoted by ⟨⟨⟨ and ⟨⟨; these symbols represent 30 and 20—the fact that they had to be taken to mean 30 and 20 *sixtieths* and not 1s, 60s or $\frac{1}{3600}$ths had to be deduced from the context.

The basic idea of decimal fractions was, in a sense, used before there was any conscious recognition of such fractions or any notation for expressing them. Thus in calculating the square root of 10, a sixteenth-century writer first multiplied by 1,000,000 and then found the square root of the 10,000,000. His result to the nearest whole number was 3,162. To obtain the square root of 10 he had next to divide by 1,000 (the square root of 1,000,000). So far he had avoided difficult fractional calculations, but here, where we would simply write down 3·162, he proceeded to divide by 1,000 and express the fractional part in sexagesimal fractions. The actual working he conveniently arranged as shown in (a); opposite each line I have indicated in (b) the

(a)   (b)

$$\begin{array}{r|l} 3 & 1\,6\,2 \\ & 6\,0 \end{array} \qquad \frac{3162}{1000} = 3 + \frac{162}{1000}$$

$$\begin{array}{r|l} 9 & 7\,2\,0 \\ & 6\,0 \end{array} \qquad \frac{162}{1000} = \frac{9720}{60 \times 1000} = \frac{9}{60} + \frac{720}{60 \times 1000}.$$

$$\begin{array}{r|l} 4\,3 & 2\,0\,0 \\ & 6\,0 \end{array} \quad \frac{720}{60 \times 1000} = \frac{43200}{60^2 \times 1000} = \frac{43}{60^2} + \frac{200}{60^2 \times 1000}$$

$$\begin{array}{r|l} 1\,2 & 0\,0\,0 \\ & \end{array} \qquad \frac{200}{60^2 \times 1000} = \frac{12000}{60^3 \times 1000} = \frac{12}{60^3}$$

significance of the corresponding steps. The final result he expressed as 3.9′.43″.12‴, i.e. $3 + \frac{9}{60} + \frac{43}{60^2} + \frac{12}{60^3}$. This procedure in finding square roots probably originated with the Hindus.

In ways similar to this, early algorists attempted to avoid awkward calculations with fractions, and so partly anticipated methods we use to-day. They failed to achieve the full advantages of modern methods through not recognizing that a system of fractions on a decimal base was implicit in what they were doing. It was, however, through attempts to avoid difficulties with fractions in calculation, rather than through methods of recording parts, that the idea of decimal fractions and notations for recording them developed.

The first work which included calculations with decimal fractions was a collection of reckoning examples by Christoff Rudolff in 1530; in this he uses a bar to separate whole numbers and fractions. The first systematic account of the use of decimal fractions was given in 1585 in a brief treatise in Dutch *De Thiende*, written by the Flemish mathematician Simon Stevin; the treatise was translated into French with the title *La Disme*. The subtitle of the treatise 'Teaching how all Computations that are met in Business may be performed by Integers alone without the aid of Fractions' shows clearly the origin of Stevin's appreciation of decimal fractions. In the accompanying extract from *La Disme* we see the notation which Stevin uses.

Explication du donné. Il y a trois ordres de nombres de Disme, desquels le premier 27(0)8(1)4(2)7(3), le deuxiesme 37(0)6(1)7(2)5(3), le troisiesme 875(0)7(1)8(2)2(3)

Explication du requis. Il nous faut trouver leur somme. *Construction.* On mettra les nombres donnez en ordre comme ci joignant, les aioustant selon la vulgaire maniere d'aiouster nombres entiers, en ceste sorte:

	(0)	(1)	(2)	(3)
	2	7	8	4	7
	3	7	6	7	5
8	7	5	7	8	2
9	4	1	3	0	4

His 27(0)8(1)4(2)7(3) is a clumsy way of expressing 27·847 but in his worked example, by using only column headings, he achieves the advantages of the modern notation. In the sixteenth and seventeenth centuries various notations were used in writing decimal fractions. In some 27·847 would have been written as 27847 or 27 | 847; these forms are essentially the same as the present form and show a full appreciation of the use of place value. Stevin's and similar notations were also used; such notations, in which each digit in the fractional part was labelled, suggest an incomplete appreciation of the principle of place value. The present notation with the decimal point was generally adopted early in the eighteenth century.

It may seem surprising that the use of decimal fractions followed so long after the use of the abacus and the introduction of a numeral system with place values. To use decimal fractions with the abacus it is only necessary to introduce columns below or to the right of those used for units; even the notation for decimal fractions requires only the extension of the principle of place values to apply to descending as well as ascending orders. In considering the long delay we must again remember that manipulating fractional parts gave much more difficulty to the human mind than manipulating whole numbers and, further, that whereas ideas of sub-units and unit fractions would arise from everyday affairs, the ideas of decimal fractions would arise only in mathematical procedure. To those who really appreciate the principle of place value, and can conceive of its being applied to descending as well as ascending values, the system of decimal fractions has enormous value. As well as facilitating calculations with and comparison of fractional parts, it also greatly simplifies numerical tables involving fractional values. The invention of logarithms in the seventeenth century and the introduction of the French decimal measures in the nineteenth century greatly extended the use of decimal fractions; the metric system is, of course, a system of sub-units with a decimal base.

The Invention of Logarithms

The use of logarithms—the second of the recent developments referred to—facilitates calculation by greatly reducing the work involved. For the benefit of the non-mathematical reader, it may be helpful to give some explanation of the use of logarithms. For this purpose the following simple table, with the base 2, will suffice.

$$2 = 2^1 \qquad\qquad 32 = 2^5$$
$$4 = 2^2 \text{ (i.e. } 2 \times 2) \qquad 64 = 2^6$$
$$8 = 2^3 \text{ (i.e. } 2 \times 2 \times 2) \qquad 128 = 2^7$$
$$16 = 2^4 \text{ (i.e. } 2 \times 2 \times 2 \times 2) \qquad 256 = 2^8$$

The following calculations illustrate the basic ideas involved:

(a) $4 \times 16 = 2^2 \times 2^4$ (from the table)
$\qquad = 2^6 \qquad$ (since $2^2 \times 2^4$ means $2 \times 2 \times 2 \times 2 \times 2 \times 2$)
$\qquad = 64 \qquad$ (from the table)

(b) $128 \div 16 = 2^7 \div 2^4$ (from the table).
$$= 2^3 \quad \text{(since } 2^7 \div 2^4 = \frac{2 \times 2 \times 2 \times 2 \times 2 \times 2 \times 2}{2 \times 2 \times 2 \times 2})$$
$\qquad = 8 \qquad$ (from the table)

(c) $\qquad 8^2 = (2^3)^2$
$\qquad\quad = 2^6 \quad$ (since $(2^3)^2$ means $2^3 \times 2^3$)
$\qquad\quad = 64$

(d) $\sqrt[3]{64}$ $= \sqrt[3]{2^6}$
$\phantom{\sqrt[3]{64}} = 2^2$ (since $2^2 \times 2^2 \times 2^2 = 2^6$)
$\phantom{\sqrt[3]{64}} = 4.$

These examples show how the results of multiplying, dividing, raising to powers and extracting roots can be obtained by the simpler processes of adding, subtracting, multiplying and dividing the corresponding indices or logarithms, the conversion to and from expression in logarithmic form being carried out by using tables. These principles apply to logarithms with any base. In our common logarithms the base 10 is used and as

$$10^1 = 10, 10^2 = 100, 10^3 = 1,000, \ldots$$

we have 1, 2, 3, . . . as the logarithms of 10, 100, 1,000. . . . We are enabled to deal with numbers other than 10, 100, 1,000, by the extension of the conception of an index or logarithm to cover fractional and negative indices. With the original meaning of an index, $10^{\frac{1}{2}}$ and 10^{-2} are meaningless, but if with $10^{\frac{1}{2}} \times 10^{\frac{1}{2}}$ we proceed as in example (a) we have

$$10^{\frac{1}{2}} \times 10^{\frac{1}{2}} = 10^1,$$

i.e. $10^{\frac{1}{2}}$ may be taken to represent $\sqrt{10}$ i.e. $3 \cdot 162$—the number which when multiplied by itself gives 10. Similarly we may take

$$10^5 \times 10^{-2} = 10^3,$$

i.e. 10^{-2} may be taken to represent $\dfrac{10^3}{10^5}$ or $\dfrac{1}{10^2}$, i.e. $\cdot 01$.

With these two extensions of the idea of indices it is possible to express any number as a power of ten; the framework of this expression is outlined below.

Number	$\cdot 01$	$\cdot 03162$	$\cdot 1$	$\cdot 3162$	1	$3 \cdot 162$	10	$31 \cdot 62$
Index or Logarithm to base 10	-2	$-1\frac{1}{2}$	-1	$-\frac{1}{2}$	0	$\frac{1}{2}$	1	$1\frac{1}{2}$

Number	100	$316 \cdot 2$	1,000
Index or Logarithm to base 10	2	$2\frac{1}{2}$	3

The discovery of logarithms can be regarded as the result of deliberate invention by John Napier of Merchiston in

Scotland. Napier's original invention differed considerably from modern logarithms; in his tables logarithms decreased as numbers increased, and zero was the logarithm of 10,000,000. His initial aim was to devise a method for finding the product of two sines and thereby simplify trigonometrical work in astronomy. It was not until his work was well advanced that Napier became aware of its wider possibilities, and it is probably true to say that his success was considerably due to the tenacity with which he adhered to his original aim and resisted the temptation to turn to larger projects before this had been achieved. Trigonometrical tables at that time did not involve fractional parts as ours do. To-day the sine of an angle is a *ratio*;

thus we take sine of 50° as $\frac{a}{b}$. In Napier's time the sine of an angle was the *length* of the perpendicular drawn in a circle of some convenient radius; thus sine 50° was measured by p. As 10,000,000 was frequently used as the length of the radius the values in the tables of sines, though expressed as integers, corresponded to those in modern seven-figure tables.

Napier's first approach was based on his knowledge of geometrical progressions. In the geometrical progression 1, 2, 4, 8 . . . in which each term is obtained by multiplying the preceding one by 2, the *product* of any two terms say 8 and 32 is itself a term, viz. 256.

(0)	(1)	(2)	(3)	(4)	(5)	(6)	(7)	(8) . . .
1	2	4	8	16	32	64	128	256 . . .

If we label the terms as shown we find that the label of 256, viz. (8) is the *sum* of the labels of the two terms. Hence to multiply two terms in such a series we need only to add the 'label numbers' and read off the number in the series corresresponding to their sum. In this series, however, there are large gaps and the gaps increase as we proceed. Napier decided to start his series with a large number and to multiply repeatedly by a fraction thereby producing a descending series in which the gaps were small and became progressively smaller. He took as his starting value 10,000,000 which was the sine of 90°, since for 90° the perpendicular coincides with the radius, and proposed to build up a series by continued multiplication by the fraction $\frac{9,999,999}{10,000,000}$. In this way he planned to obtain a descending series of numbers, each with a label giving the number of multiplications by $\frac{9,999,999}{10,000,000}$, and with the differences between consecutive terms all less than 1. As no sine can have a value greater than the radius there would be a term in this series corresponding very closely to the sine value given in the tables. Hence it would be possible to find a label number or 'artificial number' as Napier at first called them for the sine of each angle and to multiply sines by adding these numbers. Instead of multiplying by $\frac{9,999,999}{10,000,000}$ Napier obtained each term by subtracting $\frac{1}{10,000,000}$ th part of the preceding term from itself. This considerably reduced the work involved but even so, he found the work of producing such a series prohibitive. It was, however, this idea of carrying out repeated multiplication by a process of repeated subtraction that probably led him to his second approach. In this he represented values geometrically, marking points along one line corresponding to the terms of the series, and points along a second line corresponding to the number of multiplications; the points on the first line were obtained by repeatedly cutting off the same fraction of what was left of the line. The importance of this geometrical approach was that it gave a more general picture than the series of numbers had done, and led to the idea of continuous change, i.e. to the idea of a point moving along the first line with decreasing velocity, while a point moved steadily along the second line, measuring time continuously and not just counting the number of operations.

We cannot here trace the way in which Napier with these new conceptions and his proposition that 'the logarithms of similarly proportioned sines are equidifferent' proceeded to calculate the table of logarithms of sines. This table was given in his *Descriptio* (Mirifici Logarithmorum Canonis Descriptio) which was published in Edinburgh in 1614. It should, however, be seen from the above account that Napier produced his table without having any real conception of a base. We are reminded of his original approach by the word 'logarithm' which Napier introduced to replace 'artificial number'. 'Logarithm' signified 'the number of the ratios', i.e. the number of times the initial number had been multiplied by the given ratio. The idea of modern logarithms was born in this work by Napier. Following this vital beginning, more convenient ways of applying the idea were devised, and in this further work a prominent part was played by Napier himself and by Henry Briggs, Professor of Geometry in Gresham College, London, who became a friend of Napier. There are two important differences between Napier's original logarithms and present-day common logarithms. Firstly, the latter may be considered to start from 1, instead of 10,000,000, and consequently it is 1 which has the label or logarithm 0. Secondly, instead of the

multiplier $\dfrac{9,999,999}{10,000,000}$, modern logarithms have a *base* 10.

The logarithm of a number is thus not the number of multiplications but the power or index to which the base 10 has been raised. This fits our decimal system much more conveniently. Both of these modifications were to some extent foreseen by Napier. They would, however, have led to considerable complication and confusion if introduced at an earlier stage. For the initial work the large starting value repeatedly reduced by multiplication was an essential feature; it was not until the initial work was completed that improvements could usefully be contemplated. As Lord Moulton wrote in 1914 in his interesting contribution to the Napier Tercentenary Memorial Volume, 'It is an example of the truth that from the top of the mountain one can often see how the climb might have been made easier by deviations which to the climbers might well seem to be courting unnecessary difficulties.'

Conclusion

Having traced the development of man's use of number from his early very limited sense of number to the use of the present decimal system and modern methods of calculation, we may now look at some of the inconsistencies and disadvantages in our present number system, and consider how they might have been avoided had the system been devised by a modern scientific planner planning it as a whole.

Number words

1. The number words
     eleven, twelve, thirteen . . . eighteen, nineteen
   do not conform to the pattern of the other sets of words, e.g.
     sixty-one, sixty-two . . . sixty-eight, sixty-nine.
   Consistency would require
     ten-one, ten-two, ten-three . . . ten-eight, ten-nine.

2. There are irregularities in the names for the multiples of ten,
     ten, twenty, thirty, forty . . . eighty, ninety.
   This could be overcome by having instead
     onety, twoty, threety, forty . . . eighty, ninety
   (fifty and similar modifications might be permitted on grounds of euphony).
   An alternative which would keep the meanings of the words even more in evidence would be
     ten, two-ten, three-ten . . . eight-ten, nine-ten.

3. In our naming of the powers of ten, viz.:

> *ten, hundred, thousand, ten thousand, hundred thousand, million,*

new words are introduced in a rather haphazard way. In a planned scheme we might have new words only introduced when necessary, e.g.,

> *ten, hundred, ten hundred, 'newdred', ten newdred, hundred newdred,*

(where *'newdred'* signifies a hundred hundred, i.e. 10,000) or as in the Hindu system there might be different single names for each power of ten, e.g.,

> *ten, hundred, thousand, 'newdred', 'extrand', million.*

From some points of view, e.g., the use of logarithms, it would be an advantage to have words which indicate the power of ten (e.g., *'tenthird'* or *'powthree'* for a thousand).

The irregularities referred to in our system of number words probably trouble us very little; they do, however, cause difficulty to those learning our language.

Number symbols

The most desirable features of single number symbols are that they should be distinctive and easy to write. A carefully planned system would not have symbols which, like our 3 and 5, are liable to be confused when written quickly. It would be an added advantage to have a clear connexion between the form of each number symbol and the number which it represents. This would not be easy to achieve. Our planner might attempt to have the number of strokes in each symbol equal to the number represented. This would to some extent combine the advantages of tally and code symbols, though it is doubtful if nine such symbols could be devised which would be both distinctive and easy to write.

Base

It is unlikely that anyone deliberately planning a number system would decide to use the base 10; a duodecimal system (i.e. base 12) would be a more probable choice. For such a system two more symbols would be needed, i.e. there would be eleven single code symbols e.g., 1, 2, 3, 4, 5, 6, 7, 8, 9, $\triangleright$, $\perp$. In writing numbers greater than eleven the second place would be used to denote the number of twelves, the third place the number of twelve twelves, and so on. Thus twelve would be written 10 and the number of this page 94 (nine twelves and four). As twelve is an exact multiple of 3, 4 and 6 as well as of 2, division by these numbers would be simplified; there would be less carrying and fewer fractional results, e.g., $10 \div 3$ would equal 4 and $100 \div 6$ would equal 20. Further, the fractions $\frac{1}{2}$, $\frac{1}{3}$, $\frac{1}{4}$, and $\frac{1}{6}$ would be expressed in the form 0·6, 0·4, 0·3, 0·2, but $\frac{1}{5}$ and $\frac{1}{10}$ would be expressed in recurring form. The advantages of such a system would be the greater if all systems of weights and measures were also duodecimal. But however advantageous a duodecimal number system might be, it must be realized that its introduction in a civilization where a decimal system is deeply rooted would be very difficult to accomplish. A change which, for example, would lead to the replacement of 33 on a signpost by 29, to the number of runs in cricket at present described as a century being recorded as 84, and to the relationship now expressed by $6 \times 14 = 84$ being expressed instead by $6 \times 12 = 70$, would take considerable time and effort to assimilate, and would result in much confusion during the transition period.

Clearly the modern number system was not devised by a scientific planner; it does not conform completely to a consistent pattern nor are all its features designed to give the maximum convenience in present-day usage. It is the result of gradual evolution over the centuries and having 'grown' gradually it still contains many relics of earlier forgotten customs. It is not an ideal system but it is a very considerable achievement and is to be preferred to any other described in this book.

BIBLIOGRAPHY

There is some reference to the development of man's use of number in several of the histories of mathematics and other general works on mathematics. The following are particularly useful:

1. *History of Mathematics.* D. E. Smith. Ginn & Co.
   (Vol. I (1923) gives a general survey, in chronological periods, of the progress of mathematics.)
   (Vol. II (1925) gives a survey of the growth of various topics including the development of arithmetic.)
2. *A History of Mathematics.* F. Cajori. Macmillan (1919).
3. *A History of Elementary Mathematics.* F. Cajori. Macmillan (1917).
4. *A Short Account of the History of Mathematics.* W. W. Rouse Ball. Macmillan (1912).
5. *Makers of Mathematics.* A. Hooper. Random House (1948).
6. *Mathematics for the Million.* L. Hogben. Norton (1943).

There is also some account of man's earlier use of number in works on number and number theory such as:

7. *Number: The Language of Science.* T. Dantzig. Macmillan (1939). (Described by the author as 'A Critical Survey Written for the Cultured Non-Mathematician'.)
8. *Number Theory and Its History.* O. Ore. McGraw-Hill Book Co. Inc. (1948).

The following books and articles are of interest in connexion with topics considered in the first chapter of this book:

9. *Arithmetic in Africa.* O. F. Raum & J. A. Lauwerys. Evans Bros. (1938).
10. *The Numeral Words. Their Origin, Meaning, History and Lesson.* M. de Villiers. H. F. & G. Witherby (1923).
11. *Romance in Arithmetic. A History of our Currency, Weights and Measures and Calendar.* M. E. Bowman. University of London Press (1950).
12. Numbers and Numerical Concepts in Primitive Peoples. M. Wertheimer. A chapter in *A Source Book of Gestalt Psychology*, edited by W. D. Ellis. Humanities Press (1950).
13. 'The Early Numerals.' L. M. Bagge. An article in the *Classical Review*, Vol. XX (1906).
14. 'The Ability of Birds to "Count".' O. Koehler. An article in *The Bulletin of Animal Behaviour*, No. 9 (March, 1951).

Most of the general works listed above give some account of methods of writing numbers and of carrying out calculations. A fuller treatment of methods of writing numbers is given in:

15. *A History of Mathematical Notation* (Vol. I). F. Cajori. The Open Court Publishing Co. (1928).

The following works deal with various aspects of writing numbers and of carrying out calculations:

16. *Number Stories of Long Ago.* D. E. Smith. Ginn & Co. (1919).
17. *Numbers and Numerals.* D. E. Smith & J. Ginsburg. One of the monographs on 'The Contribution of Mathematics to Civilization,' Bureau of Publications, Teachers' College, Columbia University (1937).
18. *The Rhind Papyrus.* T. E. Peet. Bureau of Publications, Teachers' College, Columbia University (1937).
19. *The Story of Reckoning in the Middle Ages.* F. A. Yeldham. Harrap (1926).
20. *The Earliest Arithmetics in English.* Edited with introduction by Robert Steele. Humphrey Milford, Oxford University Press (1922).
    This includes: *The Crafte of Nombrynge.*
    The Art of Nombryng.
    Accomptynge by Counters.
21. *The Hindu-Arabic Numerals.* D. E. Smith and L. C. Karpinski. Ginn & Co. (1911).
22. *A Source Book in Mathematics,* edited by D. E. Smith. McGraw-Hill Book Co. Inc. (1929).
    This includes excerpts from:
    The First Printed Arithmetic, Treviso, 1478 (translated by D. E. Smith).
    The Declaration of the Profit of Arithmeticke, by Robert Recorde.
    La Disme, by Simon Stevin (translated by V. Sanford).
23. *Napier Tercentenary Memorial Volume,* edited by C. G. Knott. Longmans, Green & Co. (1915).